Quantised Accelerations:
From Anomalies to
New Physics

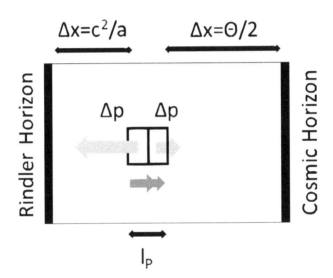

Michael Edward McCulloch

POLARIS
BOOKS

Quantised Accelerations:
From Anomalies to New Physics
Polaris Books
1100 Johnson Road
Suite 18257
Golden, CO 80402
www.polarisbooks.org

ISBN 979-8-9902823-1-5 paperback edition
ISBN 979-8-9902823-2-2 e-book

Layout and cover by Marie Stirk
All illustrations by MEMcCulloch

TABLE OF CONTENTS

The most exciting phrase to hear in science, the one that heralds new discoveries, is not "Eureka" but **"That's funny..."**
—Isaac Asimov

PREFACE
BY ROBERT ZUBRIN

THE TECHNICAL COMMUNITY is frequently confronted by maverick scientists or engineers who claim to have performed experiments that defy the established laws of physics. As exciting as such results might be, however, most people, lacking the means or time to try verify them, have generally–and in almost all cases rightly–dismissed them as artifacts of experimental error.

Mike McCulloch also challenges scientific orthodoxy with anomalous results. But his anomalies are different. Instead of being based on sensitive measurements allegedly obtained using private equipment out of public view, the anomalies that McCulloch cites are primarily well-known and widely-accepted astrophysical observations. The data he presents cannot be disputed. If current physics cannot account for them, it is not McCulloch's problem. It is physics' problem.

The leading example of this has to do with the rotation of galaxies. It has been widely observed that galaxies like our own Milky Way rotate at a speed that generates more outward centripetal acceleration than could possibly be balanced by the inward gravitational acceleration generated by their mass. So, according to standard physics, our galaxy should have flown apart long ago. The Milky Way galaxy should not exist. Yet it clearly does. This is a real problem.

In the manner of pre-Copernican astronomers adding epicycles to maintain the match between observation and the predictions offered by their Ptolemaic model of the solar system, defenders of orthodox physics have proposed to patch the galactic rotation anomaly up postulating that a hitherto unknown form of undetectable "dark matter" fills the galaxy and adds to its gravity.

There are several problems with this ad-hoc hypothesis. In the first place, despite considerable effort searching for it, no such dark matter has been detected. Secondly, there is no credible theory on how such matter could be created out of known subatomic particles. Thirdly, the centripetal acceleration at the rim of our galaxy, 2.2×10^{-10} m/s^2, is also the approximately centripetal acceleration at the rim of all other galaxies, including those differing greatly in size from the Milky Way. Even if it could be detected—which it hasn't been—the existence of dark matter could not explain that.

But get this. The speed of light, 300,000 m/s, is a fundamental physical constant manifesting itself across diverse fields of physics, including relativity, electromagnetism, and quantum mechanics. If you divide this speed by the age of the universe, 13.8 billion years or 4.35×10^{17} seconds, you obtain a fundamental acceleration of 6.93×10^{-10} m/s, which is not merely suspiciously close to the rotational acceleration of ours and all other galaxies, but within the limits of observational accuracy it is *exactly* equal to pi times it! (2.2×10^{-10} m/s^2 × p = 6.911 × 10^{-10} m/s^2.)

It sure looks like there must be some link between cosmic accelerations and galactic accelerations. The necessary explanation for this screams for new physics. In this book, McCulloch bravely sets forth to explore what that might be, and profound new capabilities that such expanded insight into nature's laws might have to offer.

The greatest scientific mystery of all, however, is not how galaxies hold together, but how the universe came to be, and why its physical laws are, very improbably, specifically aligned to allow the existence of life. Currently fashionable explanations, such as the anthropic principle and the multiverse, are antiscientific to their core. For example, a historian employing the anthropic principle to explain why the Allies won World War II, would respond by saying "because otherwise you would not able to ask the question," while one employing multiverse theory would be free to respond, "no reason, in other universes the Nazis won." Clearly such sophistry gets us nowhere.

McCulloch's theory does not answer the question of why the universe should be life-friendly either, but in my view, it points towards the right way forward. This is a similar direction to the theory advanced by physicist Lee Smolin in his 1997 book, *The Life of the Cosmos*. According to Steven Hawking, since the universe has an escape velocity of the speed of light, an outside observer might regard it as black hole. Smolin therefore argues that perhaps is what it actually is, a black hole created by the collapse of a star within a mother universe, which in turn was born as a black hole created by the collapse of a star within its mother–our grandmother–universe. Smolin speculates that each daughter universe might then have physical laws very close to–but not identical–the laws of its parent. This would allow a kind of evolution by natural selection to occur, since those universes whose physics were most favorable to the creation of stars would have the most progeny. Since stars are necessary for life, such evolution would drive the laws of physics in a life-friendly direction.

There is a lot more evidence needed to validate Smolin's theory. But, regardless, let us note the following. If the universe is a black hole with an escape velocity c, it would have an orbital velocity of $c/2^{1/2}$, and given a radius of ct, where t is the age of the universe, an object orbiting the universe at its rim would have a centripetal acceleration of $c^2/2ct = c/2t = 3.46 \times 10^{-10}$ m/s^2. This is practically the same as the centripetal acceleration at the edge of all galaxies.

Why should nearly every galaxy have the same orbital acceleration as the universe?

Surely this is worth investigating. McCulloch is showing us the way.

—Robert Zubrin
Golden, Colorado, April 14, 2024

CHAPTER 1

INTRODUCTION

IF YOU COULD go back in time and tweak one thing to speed up human progress, when would you go? I'd go back to Roman-era Alexandria.

Imagine one sunny, dusty day, you are returning home from buying bread in the agora when you hear a sound that is out of place. Curiously you go into the temple of Apollo. In the dark interior

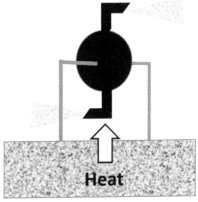

Figure 1. An aeolipile.

you see a fellow standing next to a machine spewing steam, and spinning (the machine is spinning, not the fellow). You have been lucky enough to see Hero of Alexandria with his aeolipile.

As the picture shows the aeolipile was a metal sphere full of water with an axle passing through it horizontally and two tubes sticking out of it twisted to point in opposite directions like a garden lawn sprinkler. When Hero put a fire under it, and boiled the water inside, steam spurted out of the tubes and the conservation of momentum ensured that the sphere rotated on its axle.

To the Graeco-Romans of the time, the motion of the sphere would have seemed magical and devices like this were only used in temples to impress worshippers, but imagine what might have happened if the ancient Greeks had understood the physics behind it and developed the steam engine? It would have helped them understand the relationship between dynamics, energy and heat, and quantify it.

Another Alexandrian hero of mine is John of Philoponus who in 500AD questioned Aristotle's assumption that the default state of matter is rest, and expressed a better understanding of inertia: the default state of matter is uniform speed instead. If these two fellows had been more popular, would we by now be settling Alpha Centauri?

One possible reason that these ideas were overlooked is that most of the later Greek philosophers had slaves to do their manual work for them. This had two effects, 1) they disdained the work of engineers and those who were working with their hands[1] and so lost the deep understanding of nature that the earlier Ionian Greek scientists had had, and instead focused on high-sounding but untestable metaphysics and 2) why fund the development of new machines when you could just get your slaves to do the work? (the people who had the capacity to innovate had no contact with the work, and those who did the work had no capacity or incentive to innovate). As a result of this, the Ancients ignored this dirty and noisy steam rotor, and Philoponus' insightful idea of inertia, and failed to think about the huge potential they might have. What followed, for these and other reasons, was nearly 1400 years of agonisingly slow progress (AD 100 to Copernicus in 1543 AD)

---

1   Farrington, 1944. Greek Science.

until a genuine curiosity about nature reappeared in Europe in the enlightenment.

The reason I am writing this book, is that I think we are in an era that is similar to the end of Greek science around the time of Hero or John. This is a time to which people would wish to come from our future to give us a kick up the pants. You might ask, what is our overlooked aeolipile? You will see many examples throughout this book, but probably the most central is the Casimir effect—the extraction of work from the quantum vacuum, but we will get back to that.

A major problem nowadays, is not slaves doing physicists' work for them, but computers. The amazing processing power of computers allows physicists to suggest very complex solutions to problems rather than simple ones that are more fundamental. As Douglas Adams said

> *Computers are incredibly stupid machines, but they are capable of being stupid many millions of times every second.*

The incredible processing power of computers has allowed the development of such complex fudges as dark matter, where conveniently invisible matter is packed in just where it is needed to make general relativity fit observations of galaxy rotation. As a result, astrophysicists have been able to brush under the carpet new data that does not agree with the dominant paradigm and they are devoting huge amounts of money to look for the data that the old model predicts should be there: dark matter.

This attempt to find invisible data to support a theory you learned in school is an inversion of the Popperian idea that science works best by trying to find data to disprove the present theories so we can advance to better ones. After decades of stagnation it's very clear that we need to do better than

Figure 2. Data comes before theory.

Figure 3. Physics is far from complete.

that. It is difficult to know what flawed assumptions we have—the best way to find out is to look for cases where the old theories don't work: anomalies.

We do not have far to look. I can give you a long list of anomalies that do not fit into the standard model, and in fact that is just what I am about to do! Anomalies tend to be controversial, unless they can be shoehorned into the standard model using vague hypotheses like dark matter and dark energy.

The anomalies I will discuss are not small fry. In fact the standard model at the present time, without arbitrary additions like dark matter and dark energy, only predicts 4% of the cosmos (as it is viewed by the mainstream). There is no exam you can pass with a score like that.

Of course, I am not necessarily saying that all these anomalies are correct, some of them may be due to experimental errors, but the ones I have included seem genuine and taken together they point to new physics: a deeper reformulation of physics that uses new concepts such as information horizons and Unruh radiation which are more directly testable than bent space. This new physics is relatively simple, eliminates the need for big G, very slightly modifies Newton's laws and predicts radical new applications. I will describe this new physics (quantised inertia) and show that it predicts, not 4%, but closer to 100% of what we can see.

I have already written a book that describes this new physics as it stood in 2014[2]. My intention here is to use a more empirical approach. I will first talk about the anomalies that inspired the theory, describe the theory, and then talk about the applications, including new ways to extract movement and energy from what we thought was nothing and how to get to nearby stars such as Proxima Centauri in a human lifetime.

I hope to show you how we might bring physics back to an empirical and creative phase, show how the new concepts of information and horizons fit in, get rid of harmfully-arbitrary concepts such as dark matter, and unfalsifiable theories such as string theory, solve the energy crisis and allow people to more easily leave the planet and travel through space.

To move ahead, physics will have to go back to the old methods. It is high time for The Empiricist to Strike Back.

---

2   McCulloch, M.E., 2014. Physics from the Edge. World Scientific.

CHAPTER 2

THE EMPIRICIST STRIKES BACK

The most exciting phrase to hear in science, the one that heralds new discoveries is not 'Eureka' but 'That's funny..'

—Isaac Asimov

THE MYSTERIOUS IS always exciting. We have an innate understanding that we should always look for the anomaly, because anomalies are usually game changing, and if the game's about to change it's best to know about it sooner than later.

Imagine if you were walking along, minding your own business, when suddenly a rock by the pathway rose slowly up into the sky and disappeared. This would be a hugely valuable observation, because it would suggest that something is missing from our picture of the universe, provided we make sure there is not a joker above us in a helicopter.

There are many observations today that are just as peculiar as a rock falling up into the sky, but these are being ignored, or invisible patches like dark matter and dark energy are being suggested to account for them.

If you wish to maintain the comfortable illusion that physics is complete then science is not for you, and please put this book down now, but if you are open to the inevitability that it is not complete (I'm sure it never will be!) and that there are possibilities for technology once thought impossible, and the clues for rewriting it are all around us, then read on.

In order to convince you that this approach of looking for mysterious anomalies is in fact the most efficient way to proceed we can look back in history. Science has always been driven forwards by people looking at mysterious anomalies and then thinking for a long time about them. Unfortunately, after people have spent many months or years thinking about the anomalies and putting their new theories into a logical format so others can accept them, the importance of the original anomaly is often forgotten, and the mathematical formalism is taken to be the inspiration.

For example, Einstein did not emphasise the importance of the Michelson-Morley experiment in his development[3] and this did not help the perversity of post-modern physics, which puts too little emphasis on observations and too much emphasis on theoretical consistency. Physicists became enamoured of the idea of rearranging the cosmos by thinking alone: thought experiments. So much so that nowadays this is the standard method and has led to much of physics lifting away from reality, and drifting off into the abstract seas of string theory and dark matter. Part of my reason for writing this book is an attempt to remind humanity that without looking at nature and being genuinely, uncomfortably, surprised by it, you do not advance.

One example of this is the observation by Galileo of the Moons of Jupiter in 1610. At the time it had been believed for nearly two millennia, since Plato and Aristotle had rejected the Sun-centred theory of Aristarchus, that all the planets and the

---

3   Pais. A., 1982. Subtle is the Lord. Oxford Press.

Sun orbited the Earth, which was supposed to be at the centre of the universe, an unwelcome intrusion of an emotion, namely pride, into science.

Copernicus had proposed, just before he died, that the planets orbited the Sun instead. The church did not encourage that view, the 'lack of encouragement' taking the form of being burned at the stake for heresy. Many ridiculed Copernicus's notion by saying that the Earth couldn't be moving because if it was then everything on the Earth not tied down would fall off it and leave a trail in space behind the planet, and even surely the Moon would be left behind. This was a natural complaint for people who had not listened to John Philoponus and therefore didn't know that the default state of matter is not being static in space, because as Einstein might have said "Who knows what is static anyway?", but going at constant speed. This is the idea of inertia, and that even things not tied down to the Earth are quite capable of moving along with it due to their inertia.

Then the Dutchman Hans Lippershey visited Galileo's town (at the time, Venice) with his new telescope. Galileo was pretty embarrassed not to have invented the telescope himself, and quickly crafted a telescope of his own, made a quick buck by selling one to the local prince, for to see ships afar off, and then, more usefully for science, turned it on the Moon, discovering mountains there, much to the chagrin of supporters of Aristotle who'd said the Moon was a perfect sphere.

Galileo then used the telescope to look at Jupiter. I'd say that this quick look at Jupiter did as much good for humanity as the two millennia of debate that had preceded it, because it was clear to Galileo, after a few days of looking, that Jupiter had moons and they were orbiting around it.

This was direct evidence for a start that not everything revolved around the Earth and it supported the Copernican idea that the Earth might well orbit the Sun. It even rebuffed the criticism that the Moon wouldn't follow the Earth on any orbit. If Jupiter could hold onto its Moons while orbiting whatever it was orbiting, then why not Earth? It also helped that Galileo was aware of Philoponus' writings on inertia. There is a great pleasure in observing mysteries of nature as clear as this, because all debate is bypassed by such a clear observation. It didn't do Galileo much good, since he was then under house arrest for the rest of his life, but at least he had the satisfaction of knowing that he was right.

Deep space is a great place to look for anomalies because the only processes operating there are inertia and gravity so these laws are laid bare for all to see and other complicated processes like friction are not present to muddy the waters. It is difficult to argue against data as clear as Galileo's Jupiter observations, and in fact the church of the time, which had a stranglehold on the media, could not argue against it, which annoyed them so much they had to have Galileo locked up, but his idea remained.

The second example is the case of a human not only using a chance direct observation to change a world view, but actually modifying the circumstances to test various hypotheses. This was Isaac Newton, a scientist still unsurpassed in his skill with both experiment and theory and massive contributions to maths, gravity and light.

Funny how the apple falls, but the Moon doesn't

Before Newton everyone thought that white light was pure. White still reflects purity in our culture, admittedly for different reasons of cleanliness, for example, wedding dresses are still mainly white to reflect the purity of the bride. Newton in 1665 was the first

Figure 4. Newton links the fall of an apple to the orbit of the Moon, & so discovers gravity.

to realise that white is actually a dirty old mess and the pure colours are, well, all the other ones.

It was known that when white light passed through a prism, or a jagged glass edge, a rainbow was projected onto a nearby screen, but people assumed that the glass was *making* the colours somehow from the pure white light. The experiment Newton did was to allow sunlight into a room through a small window (see the white beam below, left) and pass it through a glass prism (shown). Sure enough, colours were produced (see the shades of grey on the right). He noted that he expected to see a disc on the wall, because the light coming from the Sun comes from a disc, but he was surprised to see an oblong projected onto the wall.

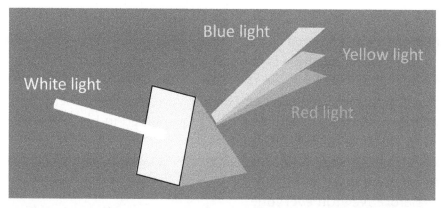

Figure 5. Newton's prism experiment. The crucial observation that a beam of light passed through a prism shows colours, but also becomes elongated.

Here then is the anomaly that set him onto his theory of colours. The reason for the oblong is that white light is made up of all the colours of the rainbow together, but they are differently bent in their path by the prism so that the neat disc that was expected to be projected onto the wall was spread out into an oblong. To prove this Newton selected just one of the colours coming out of the first prism and sent it through a second prism and showed first that the prism did not 'make' all the colours again, to disprove the earlier theory and he also measured the various colours' positions on the wall and showed that all the separate colours were bent at different angles by the prism to support his theory (see the schematic below). He called this kind of experiment an 'experimentum crucis' or crucial experiment because in it he was able to arrange things to decide without a doubt which hypothesis was correct, which intellectual path to take.

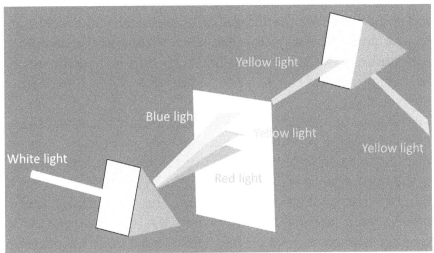

Figure 6. Newton's prism experiment. How Newton proved that prisms do not 'make' the colours in light as believed, but split white light into colours.

The third example is a negative one, but it is important to illustrate a problem that is endemic in physics today. Since 1957 the British Antarctic Survey (BAS) had been taking measurements using a spectrometer which looked up through the atmosphere at the Sun and worked out how much ultraviolet light was being absorbed by the ozone in the atmosphere. In the middle of the 1970s, BAS's ground spectrometer showed that the amount of ozone in the atmosphere was decreasing[4], but oddly enough NASA's Nimbus 7 satellite with its TOMS (Total Ozone Mapping Spectrometer) wasn't seeing any decrease in ozone at all. After the discovery of the ozone hole by BAS, NASA went back through their data and found that their TOMS instrument had indeed been seeing the ozone hole, but the satellite's computer had been programmed to reject any anomalies!

Luckily the data had only been 'flagged', so it was still available in memory, but this meant that NASA missed the discovery and it shows the danger of 'expectations' in science, ie: you shouldn't have any! You just need to look at the data and *then* think a little. It also shows the dangers of relying too much on computers, and this is a post-modern problem I will come back to.

Well, now in case you think I'm being unduly harsh on NASA here, I should tell you what my first post after my physics degree was. Just imagine, after the story I've just told you, what would be the most embarrassing thing I might have done? Well, no, I didn't do that, but I was tasked, as part of my PhD to work at the British Oceanographic Data Centre (BODC) in Liverpool, who were a great bunch of people who still do a great job of collating and storing oceanographic data. I was asked to flag data showing the vertical profile of temperature and salinity in the ocean. The word 'flag' means 'mark' data that I thought was physically anomalous. For example, if there was a huge spike in temperature at 20 metres depth without a corresponding reduction in salinity, that is unlikely because its buoyancy would be physically unstable, so it is likely to be an instrumental glitch. That is exactly what I did for hours on end for a few initial months,

---

4   Farman, J.C., B.G. Gardiner and J.D. Shanklin, 1985. Large losses of total ozone in Antarctica reveal seasonal ClOx/NOx interaction. Nature, 315, 6016, 207-210.

before I was able to move over to the university, part time, to do the research for my PhD. I felt guilty about flagging anomalies at the time, although in my case there was a valid reason. Of course, very often we spend our lifetimes atoning for our perceived sins, so this may be why I am now so keen on anomalies and why I am writing this book.

Later, at the UK's Met Office, I was put in charge of assessing their ocean model's output in map form. This time I atoned for my earlier flagging sins, by stopping the computer's interpolation and smoothing step that had always been used before, and pixelated the data instead (showing the un-interpolated numbers). Immediately I discovered something–narrow bands of freshwater on the surface of the model ocean caused, as it turned out, by rainbands. These bands of freshwater had previously been smoothed away by the software. I wrote a paper with colleagues on that[5]

The moral of these stories is–look at the messy data without any artificial filters, computational or ideological, and then think. So let us now look at some contemporary anomalies.

---

5   McCulloch, M.E., J.O.S. Alves & M.J. Bell, 2004. Modelling shallow mixed layers in the northeast Atlantic. J. Marine Systems, Vol. 52(1-4), pp 107-119.

CHAPTER 3

ENCOUNTER WITH ANOMALIES

IN THIS BOOK I will give you a summary of various anomalies known in physics, starting from the cosmic scale downwards. I should first say something nice about the standard model of physics: it is accurate in regimes we have studied for a long time in our laboratories, sometimes amazingly so as for the case of quantum electro-dynamics, but it may be largely due it having been tuned to be[6]. I tend to think of anomalies in terms of acceleration regimes. On the Earth, accelerations are on the order of 9.8 m/s^2 or within a few orders of magnitude (factors of ten) of that. The standard model seems to work at normal terrestrial and high accelerations, for example in the particle accelerator at CERN, although there are now some indications of deviation from it even there[7].

Where the standard model fails uniformly is in low acceleration regimes, and by low, I mean in which the acceleration is on the order of 2×10^{-10} m/s^2. To put this acceleration in context: it is tiny. If you were to accelerate at this rate you would go from zero to 60 mph in 4280 years, something you are unlikely

6   Unzicker, A., 2013. The Higgs Fake.

7   Krasznahorkay et al. (2016). Physical Review Letters 116, 042501

to see in a car advert. The acceleration also implies a change from zero to the speed of light in something not too far from the age of the universe, which in itself is intriguing. It makes the world of snails look positively frenetic. You might think, so what? Why should we be bothered by such an extreme regime? The reason is that most of the universe is in that regime, being far from a gravity well, and in the past 50 years those are the regions we have been seeing for the first time, with advances in observing technology like the Hubble and James Webb telescopes and they are also the regions that standard physics just cannot predict.

CHAPTER 4

GUIDELINES FOR ANOMALY HUNTING

General principles for people who are interested in anomalies.

1. Just because an anomaly is listed here does not mean it definitively disproves the present model. It could be due to an artefact: a mundane effect that we have forgotten to consider. I have been careful to choose solid anomalies, but no-one is infallible.

2. Often anomalies can be hidden, by people who like the dominant paradigm, using arbitrary fudges that are unlikely but they say 'at least follow the present paradigm'. Dark matter is an example.

3. Many of the anomalies listed here will be savagely criticised by some. That's part of the game. As Captain Kirk once said, "You have to be willing to take risks if you want to sit in that chair." Please refer to point 1 on this page.

4. Although anomalies can be a gamble, one anomaly is worth 1000 confirmations of the theory because they can be game-changing. So it is worth a look if the chance of it being solid is greater than 0.1%.

5. One way to find anomalies is to notice what people are uncomfortable talking about. This is difficult because they don't talk about it!
6. Occasionally, real anomalies have been deliberately associated with conspiracy theories to discredit them.
7. If you love anomalies, do not expect to be popular!

CHAPTER 5

AN ANOMALY A DAY

5.1 LOW-L CMB ANOMALY

The Cosmic Microwave Background is too smooth on large scales.

The Cosmic Microwave Background, CMB[8], is a radiation detected in space that looks as if it comes from objects with a temperature of 2.725K (K=Kelvin). Recent satellites launched to look at it, such as the Cosmic Background Explorer (COBE), the Wilkinson Microwave Anisotropy Probe (WMAP) and Planck[9] have shown that the

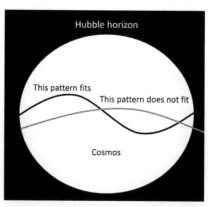

Figure 7. Cosmic sized patterns are damped.

---

8   Penzias and Wilson, 1964.

9   Planck Collaboration, 2014. Planck 2013 results: CMB power spectrum and likelihood. Astronomy and Astrophysics, 571, A15.

pattern of this radiation is far too smooth on the largest scales, the Hubble scale, as if some process is damping large scale patterns. This may be akin to the way that long waves cannot easily form in a short bath (see the diagram). As with most of these anomalies, I will later discuss the theory that predicts this[10].

The Planck data showed that the energy in the spectrum is 5-10% lower on the largest scales, than expected according to the standard model (called Lambda-CDM). This anomaly is significant at the 2.5-3 sigma level, which means that it is not yet conclusive, which requires significance at the 5 sigma level.

We also need to consider all objections eg: Robataille who argues that the CMB is a signal from the Earth's ocean.[11]

5.2 DIRAC'S MASS-RADIUS RELATION

The radius of an object squared divided by its mass is a constant number.

It was first postulated in 1937 by Dirac, see the discussion in[12] that the following relation will hold

$$\frac{r_p^{\,2}}{m_p} = \frac{r_u^{\,2}}{m_u} = K$$

This means that the radius of a proton (r_p) squared divided by its mass (m_p) is equal to the radius of the cosmos (r_u) squared, divided by its mass (m_u) and also equal to a constant number, K.

Putting in the numbers for other objects we can see that this is more or less correct. Here are a few examples:

---

10   McCulloch, M.E., 2014. A toy cosmology using a Hubble-scale Casimir effect. Galaxies, 2(1), 81-88.

11   Robataille, P-M., 2007. WMAP: A radiological analysis. Progress in Physics, Vol. 1.

12   Dirac, P.A.M., 1937. The Cosmological Constants. *Nature*. 139 (3512): 323. See also the discussion in Unzicker, A., 2019. The Mathematical Reality.

Object	Radius (m)	Mass (kg)	Radius²/mass
The Observable Cosmos	4.4×10^{26}	$10^{53 \pm 1}$	0.19 to 19
Milky Way	10^{21}	10^{41}	10
Solar system (Oort cloud)	20,000 AU[13]s	2×10^{30}	4.5
Proton	0.84×10^{-15}	1.67×10^{-27}	0.0004
Electron	2.8×10^{-15}	9.1×10^{-31}	8.6

As you can see the relation works quite well for the cosmos as a whole, for the Milky Way, the Solar system (but only if you take its edge to be the Oort cloud) and for electrons. These are all coherent systems. It works much less well for protons, which is ironic as that was Dirac's first suggestion. Maybe the proton is not as pure as it makes out!

5.3 DIRAC LARGE NUMBERS HYPOTHESIS

Dirac found that the ratio 'universe radius / proton radius' is 10^{39} and the ratio 'universe mass / proton mass' is the square of that.

When you calculate both the electromagnetic and gravitational forces in the simplest atom, hydrogen, then the ratio between them is about 10^{40}. This means the electromagnetic force is larger than gravity to an astronomical degree!

At about the same time Erwin Hubble was measuring the size of the cosmos using supernovae, and determined that it was about 10^{22} metres, later corrected to about 10^{26} metres and the proton radius is about 10^{-15} metres. The ratio between these two numbers is 10^{41}. To rephrase A. Unzicker "*Such large*

---

13   AU = an Astronomical Unit = 1.5×10^{11}m

numbers appear nowhere else, but here they agree"[14] (10^{41} is close enough to 10^{40} given the uncertainties in these parameters).

This might be a coincidence, but there is a third coincidence that makes it more likely to be something deep. When Dirac calculated the implied mass of the cosmos, by counting up the visible matter in it, it was about 10^{53}kg. The mass of the proton is 1.67×10^{-27}kg. When you calculate the ratio of these numbers you get about 10^{80}. Interestingly, this is the square of 10^{40}. And there is reason to think that mass might be related to the square of the radius, the surface area, rather than the volume—it does for black holes.

5.4 COSMIC ACCELERATION

Another phenomenon not predicted by the standard model was the surprise discovery in 1999 that the universe was not only expanding with a constant velocity as found by Hubble, but that that expansion was apparently accelerating. This acceleration was discovered[15] by looking at type-II supernovae. Supernovae are stars that run out of fuel, their core collapses and for some unknown reason they then explode spectacularly, often outshining the galaxies they are in. The key point is that these explosions are (assumed to be) of the same intrinsic brightness, which means that if you're standing at the same distance away (preferably a few light years!) they would be of the same brightness. The discoverers noticed that the supernovae very far away were unexpectedly (lovely word!) faint. Other groups have looked for systematic errors such as obscuration of the light by dust, but have found nothing amiss, so

---

14   Unzicker, A., Einstein's Lost Key, 2015. Pages 150-155.

15   Riess, A.G.; et al., 1998. Observational Evidence from Supernovae for an Accelerating Universe and a Cosmological Constant. *The Astronomical Journal.* 116 (3): 1009–1038.

the easiest way to explain this observation is if the cosmos has recently accelerated.

Imagine leaving a harbour on a ship and looking back at the lights in the night slowly moving away from you. You turn around for a minute, look back, and the lights are very far away. You would probably conclude the ship had accelerated.

This is a thing that is easy to say, but to see what a howling shock this should be to standard physics, the mass of the cosmos is about 10^{53} kg. This mass is not to be sneezed at, and the huge amount of energy required to accelerate it away from its own gravity, as has been observed, is about 20 times greater than all the mass-energy we can see in the cosmos. This means that the standard model only predicts about one part in twenty of the mass-energy that is 'apparently' out there, or 4-5%, so the standard model, is one of the least successful models ever made, when you consider its success with respect to the environment in which it is supposed to be valid.

5.5 DARK FILAMENTS ALIGNED WITH GALACTIC SPIN

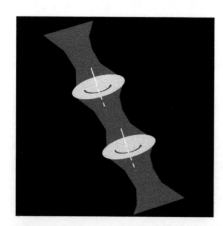

Figure 8. Filaments between galaxies.

Filaments that bend light (& look like dark matter) tend to extend away from the spin axes of disc galaxies.

Most of the galaxies that exist, shown on the schematic as white ellipses, lie within what are called 'filaments'. These are lines (see the grey) along which background light is bent as if there is matter there bending it by gravity, but no matter can be seen. The cosmic web is the name given to these filaments which extend throughout the cosmos.

Tempel et al.[16] ('et al.' means 'and others') showed that disc galaxies–those that spin in the traditional sense, have their spin axes, which are shown by the white lines above, aligned along the filaments.

It is different for elliptic galaxies, which are a little more like swarms of chaotic bees than spinning systems. They have their (weak) spin axes aligned perpendicular to those filaments. As usual this makes no sense at all. Although perhaps it could be due to the emission of material along galactic axis–galactic jets, or to provide a spoiler, the loss of inertial mass along spin axes[17].

5.6 SUPERLUMINAL GALACTIC JETS

Some galactic jets may be moving faster than light.

This is a controversial one and may well get me into some jets of hot water, but it is fascinating. Some active galaxies or quasars, for reasons known only to themselves, so far, emit relativistic jets from their centres in both directions

Figure 9. A galactic jet.

along their rotation axes. See the jets in the schematic:

The amount of energy required to create these jets doesn't bear thinking about. The best explanation that physics can

---

16   Tempel E., R. S. Stoica, E. Saar, 2013. Evidence for spin alignment of spiral and elliptical/S0 galaxies in filaments. Monthly Notices of the Royal Astronomical Society, Vol. 428, Issue 2, 11, Pages 1827–1836.

17   McCulloch, M.E., 2008. Modelling the flyby anomalies using a modification of inertia. MNRAS-Letters, 389(1), L57-60.

provide at the moment is more invisible magic: spinning central galactic black holes, in this case.

The mystery is even deeper: blobs of matter within the jets appear to be moving faster than light[18] [19] but before we get too excited, Rees[20], showed that, due to relativity, if they are pointing roughly at us then jets can appear to move faster than light, without doing so. However, if these particular jets were indeed pointing at us then they would appear on average to be shorter and they do not. Also, the most famous of the jets, that of M87, has an angle to us of 44-64° and to make its jet slow to light speed you'd have to assume it has an implausible angle of 20°. So, superluminal jets? See also the similar spin-axial behaviour in section 5.5, and the spoiler.

5.7 THE TULLY-FISHER RELATION

The luminosity (L) of a galaxy (or visible mass) is proportional to the fourth power of its stars' orbital speed. Physics does not predict this.

Astronomers find the absolute mass of a galaxy by looking at its apparent brightness, scaling this up to account for its distance, and then counting the number of Suns it contains. If you multiply by the known mass of our Sun then you get the likely total mass. Further, astronomers can use the variation in the Doppler shift in the light coming from the galaxy to determine the stars' orbital speed, since some will be moving away and some closer, so the Doppler shift will spread the light into a spectrum.

18   Porcas, R., 1983. Superluminal motion—astronomers still puzzled. *Nature*, 302, 753-754.

19   Biretta, J.A., et al., 1999. Hubble space telescope observations of superluminal motion in the M87 jet. The Astrophysical Journal, 520, 2, 621-626.

20   Rees, M.J., 1966. Appearance of relativistically expanding radio sources. Nature, 211, 468-470.

In 1977 Tully and Fisher[21] noticed that the orbital speed of the stars on the outskirts of galaxies, was proportional to the fourth power of the luminosity of the whole galaxy (actually somewhere between the powers of 3.5 and 4) and

Figure 10. A spinning galaxy.

therefore the mass of the galaxy. This relation works very well, yet there is nothing in standard physics that predicts it.

This relation is now used to estimate the distance to galaxies, because one can measure the Doppler shift and therefore the orbital speed accurately, and then use the relation to determine the luminosity. The apparent brightness of the galaxy then allows you to determine its distance.

5.8 GALAXY CLUSTER PROBLEM

Galaxy clusters have too much kinetic energy to be bound, but are!

This was first noticed by a delightfully eccentric fellow called Fritz Zwicky in 1933. He'd been looking at galaxy clusters, collections of galaxies bound together by gravity (see the schematic) and he found that, given the gravitational mass he could see, and the fast speed of them, gravity should be unable to hold on to them and so these clusters should be flying apart. The fact that the galaxies were together meant that either by chance they had collected, which looked unlikely, or that something funny was going on.

---

21   R.B. Tully and J.R. Fisher, 1977. A new method of determining distance to galaxies. Astronomy and Astrophysics, 661-673.

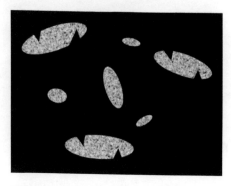

Figure 11. Schematic of a cluster of galaxies.

Zwicky [22] proposed that there was dark matter in them that we could not see but which held them together with its gravity.

Yes, Zwicky was the first to suggest the awful dark matter, but we can forgive him because he discovered the anomaly itself and he was delightfully eccentric. He used to carry around a petition that people could sign to request he be given a Nobel prize and he used to call his astronomical colleagues 'spherical bastards' since he said they were bastards no matter which way you looked at them.

5.9 GALAXY ROTATION PROBLEM

Stars at the edge of galaxies orbit too fast to be gravitationally bound.

In the 1980s Rubin and Ford[23] used the Doppler shift to look at the orbit of stars in the Andromeda galaxy and found that outside a radius of around 8 kpc (a parsec is about 3×10^{16} meters) the rotation speed was constant. According to Newton's laws the orbital speed should drop off with radius because an orbit is a balance between gravity pulling in and the inertial/centrifugal force pushing out.

---

22 Zwicky, F., 1933. Die Rotverschiebung von extragalaktischen Nebeln [The red shift of extragalactic nebulae]. *Helvetica Physica Acta.* 6: 110–127.

23 Rubin, V.C.; Ford, W. Kent, Jr., 1970. Rotation of the Andromeda Nebula from a Spectroscopic Survey of Emission Regions. The Astrophysical Journal. 159: 379–403.

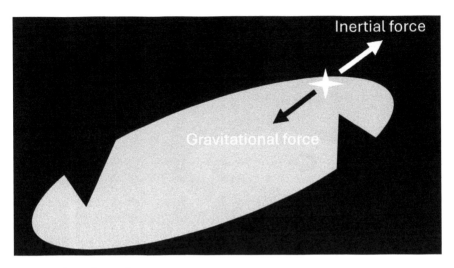

Figure 12. A disc galaxy.

This schematic shows a galaxy (the grey oval) and a star within it (white star), subject to a centrifugal inertial force outwards (the grey arrow) and an attractive gravitational force inwards (the black arrow).

Further out the centrifugal force required to balance the weaker inwards gravitational pull can be lower, and so the orbital speed can also be lower.

Oddly, the observations showed no such thing. Stars on the periphery orbited far too fast. For 40 years, people have been searching for the dark matter they believe is hidden inside these galaxies, including in our galaxy and therefore near us, to hold their outsides in, with very expensive detectors in mines, in the ice and even up in space, but they have not found it.

What if instead of boosting gravity, we reduce inertia?—but again I am jumping the gun...

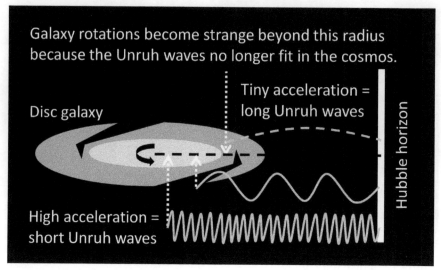

Figure 13. Unruh waves and the galactic cut-off radius.

5.10 GALACTIC CUTOFF.

Galaxy rotation 'breaks' below accelerations of about 2×10^{-10} m/s^2.

The acceleration of stars within galaxies is high near the centre as they move quickly around a smaller, tighter circle. The acceleration reduces as you go out. It was pointed out by Milgrom [24] that as soon as the acceleration gets down to 2×10^{-10} m/s^2, then that is where problems begin. I call this Milgrom's break as he vaguely suggested there might be a "break in the response of the vacuum at this point".

In the schematic above, you can see a galaxy (light core, grey periphery) and the Unruh wavelengths [25] seen by stars at

---

24   Milgrom, M., 2005. In Mass profiles and shapes of cosmological structures. G. Mamon, F. Combes, C. Deffayet, B. Fort (Eds.). EAS Publications Series Vol. 20, EDP Sciences, Lex Ulix Cedex A, p 217.

25   Unruh radiation is seen by accelerating objects. See Unruh (1976), Davies (1975) and Fulling (1973).

various radii (the waves). In the centre the acceleration (a) is high and the Unruh wavelength, given by λ=c²/a (c is the speed of light) is short, as shown by the wave at the bottom. Further out, the acceleration is lower so the wavelength is longer (the curve above the first). At exactly the radius at which the Unruh waves are as big as the Hubble scale, see the dashed wave, then that is where the anomalies begin.

This proves unambiguously that this anomaly has something to do with Unruh radiation. For the answer, see later in this book!

5.11 GLOBULAR CLUSTER ROTATION PROBLEM

Small congregations of stars (globular clusters) show flat velocity curves just like larger galaxies do, but can't contain dark matter.

Within galaxies themselves, are much smaller congregations of stars called globular clusters. Their stars orbit around a common centre more like swarms of bees than rotating discs, so they have a dispersion curve instead of a rotation curve. Now, the hypothesis of dark matter has an Achilles heel—to make it work in galaxies they must specify new physics to force the darks to stay spread out to avoid it all ending up in the galactic centre. This means that they can't squash it into smaller systems. This is why Scarpa et al.[26] decided to look at the orbital speed of stars in globular clusters, to see if there was a similar problem. If there was, then dark matter was dead. In short, there was a problem as shown in the plot.

The orbital speed of the stars in the cluster at first reduces from the centre as expected, but right of the vertical grey line

26   Scarpa, R., G. Marconi, R. Gilmozzi and G. Carrano, 2007. Using globular clusters to test gravity in the weak acceleration regime. The Messenger, 128 ,41-.

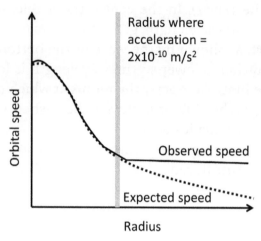

Figure 14. The typical rotation curve of a globular cluster (simplified).

the observed rotation curve diverges from that expected. This is not in agreement with Newton or general relativity. Even more interesting, the divergence point is at the same rotational acceleration, of 2×10^{-10} m/s^2, as in galaxies and elsewhere.

Taken together with wide binaries and Proxima Centauri, also discussed in this book, this is compelling evidence that dark matter is not the solution to the galaxy rotation problem.

5.12 QUASARS ARE NOT TIME DILATED

Quasars are thought to be very far away, so if the cosmos is expanding they should show relativistic time dilation. They don't!

Quasars, or Quasi-Stellar objects were discovered back in the 1950s and more than a million of them have been found. They are thought to be very active galaxies, very far away, and since they are apparently still so bright, the present idea is that they are powered by a central black hole which emits radio waves with incredible amounts of energy.

Most quasars have a very high redshift and since the cosmos is thought to be expanding this is also taken to mean that they are far away and fast moving (it is assumed their light has been Doppler shifted). So, according to special relativity, they should show time dilation when we look at them. This means that everything they do should appear to be in slow motion.

Astronomers had already checked time dilation using supernovae. They looked at the duration of their explosions and saw that distant ones played out more slowly, supporting relativistic time dilation & cosmic expansion.

Hawkins [27] tried this with Quasars. Since they are not explosions, he simply looked at the rate at which their brightness varied in time and he found that there was no slowdown in the rate of variation with distance and therefore there was no apparent time dilation! This is a deeply unsettling result for the standard cosmology and the result supports, to some extent, the conclusions of Halton Arp (see the next page) who claimed that quasars are not distant objects at all and that their high redshift is due to something else, something intrinsic, and a possibility will be discussed later in this book.

If cosmic redshift is not solely due to recession speeds then the present Big Bang cosmological model falls apart.

5.13 ARP'S INTRINSIC REDSHIFT

The high redshift of quasars may not be due to their recession speed away from us, but from new physics.

The frequency of light emitted by atoms depends on the energy released as electrons fall from higher atomic orbits to lower ones. When we look at far off astronomical objects these frequencies are shifted longer, into the red (in Figure 15

---

27   Hawkins, M.R.S., 2010. On time dilation in quasar light curves. *Mon. Not. Royal Astro. Soc.*, 405, 1940-1946.

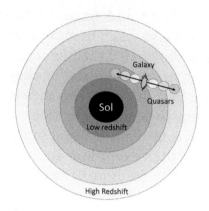

Figure 15. Redshift increases with distance, perhaps with exceptions.

redshift is shown by the lighter shade). They are said to be red-shifted. It has been assumed since the 1920s that this red-shift is caused by the Doppler shift due to their movement away from us. Quasars (active galaxies) are very red, so it has been assumed that they are far off, and since they are still bright, they must be massively energetic. Where does the energy come from? It would simplify matters if they were closer. They may be!

Halton Arp discovered several quasars at high redshift (see the small circles) that were attached to nearby low red-shift galaxies with tendrils (see the grey 'fuzz'). He concluded that the high redshift of the quasars (light shade) was not caused by their distance and Hubble-recession away from us but from something intrinsic—some new physics. He also noticed, and this is also hotly debated, that the redshift (Z) of these quasars was quantised at the values Z = 0.06, 0.3, 0.6, 0.91, 1.41, 1.96, 2.64 and perhaps 3.47.[28] and that the quasars seem to 'step down' in redshift as they move out from their host (parent?) galaxies (see the white to grey circles in what I call 'Arp's Kebab' in Fig. 15. This implies a fundamentally new process is determining the mass-energy of electrons through time. For a possible explanation, see Section 7.12.

---

28   Arp, Halton, 1998. Seeing Red: redshifts, cosmology and academic science. Apeiron Press.

5.14 THE HUBBLE TENSION

The Hubble constant has two different values depending on whether you calculate it from local galaxy recession or from the early CMB.

The sound of an object moving away from you will shift to a lower frequency as the waves from your point of view are spread out. This is the Doppler effect and applies to light waves as well. As we know, Edwin Hubble noticed that the light from distant galaxies was red shifted, that is, the wavelength of the light we received from them was longer, implying in a similar way that the galaxies were moving away from us and that the further ones were moving away faster than the closer ones. This was taken to mean that all the galaxies were moving away from a common centre as if there was an explosion 13.6 billion years in the past, the Big Bang.

Looking at local galaxies, the Hubble expansion rate is measured to be 73 km/s/Mpc. That is, galaxies one megaparsec (Mpc) away from us are apparently moving away from us at 73 km/s.

Recently, a new method was devised to calculate the Hubble constant from observations of the Cosmic Microwave Background, that represents the cosmos long ago at a redshift of Z=1000, and then extrapolating forward using standard models assuming dark matter and dark energy. Perhaps not surprisingly they got a different answer: 67.7 km/s/Mpc.

The discrepancy is now beyond a plausible level of chance, so it is significant[29] and it implies that the standard way of modelling the cosmos is wrong. Has the Hubble constant changed with time or in space?

---

29   Riess, A. et al., 2019. Large Magellanic Cloud Cepheid Standards Provide a 1% Foundation for the Determination of the Hubble Constant and Stronger Evidence for Physics beyond ΛCDM. *The Astrophysical Journal*, Volume 876, Issue 1, article id. 85, 13 pp.

5.15 COSMIC CLOCKS

All galaxies, even over a 30-fold range of scale, show a rotation period at their very edges of close to 1 billion years.

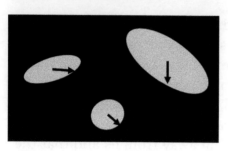

Figure 16. All galaxies rotate in around 1 billion years.

As discussed above, the orbits of stars at the edges of galaxies contradict normal physics. So much so that 10 times as much dark mass has to be added to galaxies to make general relativity predict them correctly. A recent new observation[30] is that if you take the edge stars and work out, given their apparent speed, how long they take to make one complete orbit, you find it is always about 1 billion years.

This includes galaxies with a 30-fold range of sizes and cannot be explained by standard physics that says that the acceleration of a star (a) depends upon the gravitational constant (G) times the mass of the galaxy (M) divided by its distance from the centre.

$$a = \frac{GM}{r^2}$$

Working from this and noting that the period of an orbit is equal to $\tau = \frac{2\pi r}{v}$,where v is the orbital speed, you can show that the period of the orbit should depend on the radius to the power 3/2, not to the radius directly. The fact that every galaxy is effectively co-rotating like a bunch of varisized clocks is a massive clue to something, but what? See section 7.5.

---

30   Meurer et al., 2018. Cosmic clocks: A Tight Radius–Velocity Relationship for HI-Selected Galaxies *MNRAS*, 476, 1624-1636.

5.16 THE MAGELLANIC CLOUDS' ORBIT.

The Milky Way's two companions, the Magellanic Clouds, orbit too fast to be bound, but the Magellanic Stream proves they are bound.

The Large and Small Magellanic clouds (LMC, SMC) are small galaxies close to our Milky Way galaxy (see the schematic). They have left a curved trail behind them called the Magellanic Stream (the dashed curves) which seems to show that they are gravitationally bound to the Milky Way.

So far so good, but their orbital speed is 378 km/s, and according to Newton they are moving far too fast to be bound to the Milky Way. Inertial mass should be winning the battle against gravity. "Aha," you say "you must include dark matter". When you do this it predicts a maximum bound speed of 275 km/s, still not enough[31].

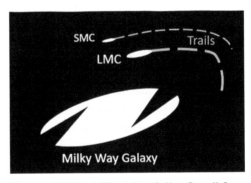

Figure 17. The Milky Way & the Small & Large Magellanic clouds.

This is similar to the galaxy rotation problem, sections 5.9 and 7.4, the globular cluster rotation problem and the wide binary orbit problem, sections 5.17 and 7.15. Anything orbiting at a very low acceleration is behaving very oddly: almost as if it had less inertial mass. For the solution to this problem, see section 7.14.

---

31   Kallivayalil, N. et al., 2013. Third-epoch Magellanic Cloud proper motions I: Hubble Space Telescope / WFC3 data and orbit implications. *The Astrophysical Journal*, 764, 161.

5.17 WIDE BINARY ORBITS

Co-orbiting wide binary stars, when their mutual acceleration is as low as at the edge of galaxies, show a similar change in behaviour.

Stars, like people, tend to pair up. Most stars are part of a binary system in mutual orbit, bound by gravity which is just strong enough to counter the 'centrifugal' or inertial force that tends to separate them as shown here

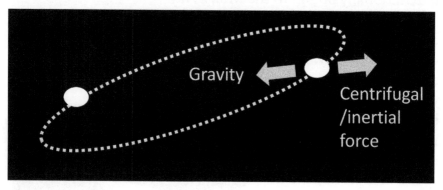

Figure 18. A wide binary system.

Hernandez et al. [32] [33] found that if these binary stars are very far apart, more than 7000 au (or 10^{15} metres) apart, then they orbit at too fast a speed. Much faster than Newton, or general relativity would predict.

This is identical to the galaxy rotation problem which has the stars at the edges of galaxies orbiting too fast, and the rotation of globular clusters as well, which are small congregations of stars within galaxies.

---

32   Hernandez, X., R.A.M. Cortes, C. Allen and R. Scarpa, 2018. Challenging a Newtonian Prediction through GAIA wide binaries. *IJMP-D*, Vol 28, Issue 8, id. 1950101. https://arxiv.org/abs/1810.08696

33   Hernandez, X., S. Cookson, R.A.M. Cortés, 2022, *MNRAS*, Vol 509, 2, 2304–2317.

This anomaly cannot be explained by dark matter since the new physics they propose for has to force it to stay spread out to predict the edges of galaxies, so it can't then be forced to congregate in these small systems.

Also, amazingly, the cut-off acceleration below which this happens is exactly the same in galaxy clusters, galaxies, globular clusters and wide binaries, the magic: 2×10^{-10} m/s^2, so we are obviously here looking at a subtle change in the deep laws of physics rather than extra matter. See section 7.15.

5.18 PROXIMA CENTAURI'S ORBIT

Newtonian physics and general relativity do not even correctly predict our nearest neighbour in space.

Our nearest star system, that of Alpha Centauri, is only 4.4 light years away so it has been well observed. It is a triple system. The inner two stars Alpha and Beta Centauri (shown below in the centre) orbit very close to each other, only 40 AUs apart, so we can use Newton's laws very well to determine their combined mass. The third star Proxima (a red dwarf) is much further out, 15,000 AUs, but it is obviously bound to A and B because it shares their proper motion through the sky and is chemically similar to them.

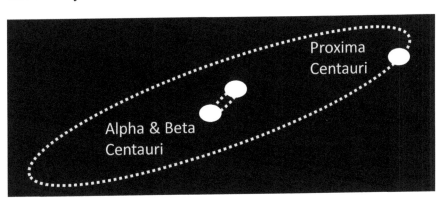

Figure 19. The Alpha Centauri system.

However, it cannot be bound because it is moving so fast in its orbit that the inertial force should be forcing it to spin off into space[34]. There is a tiny chance that we are looking at it in an extreme part of its orbit (but remember my warning in Chapter 4 about comfortable but unlikely fudges).

This may remind you of the galaxy clusters, the galaxy rotation problem, globular clusters and wide binaries in which outer stars with acceleration below 2×10^{-10} m/s^2 also orbit too fast to be bound, but are bound. Proxima's acceleration is around this critical acceleration too. Again, dark matter cannot be used to explain Proxima since to stay spread out to predict galaxies it can't then be forced to congregate in this system. All these cases are crying out for new physics linked to this very low acceleration. See section 7.17.

5.19 HOAG'S OBJECT

A distant galaxy takes the form of a central sphere of stars, surrounded by a perfect ring. Present theory cannot explain it.

Figure 20. Hoag's Object.

In 1950 Arthur Hoag discovered a very peculiar galaxy[35]. It had a yellow central core and a separate and almost perfect ring surrounding it.

One of the theories suggested to explain its weird shape was that a homicidal galaxy rammed a hole in its centre, and then

---

34   Matthews, R., G. Gilmore, 1993. Is Proxima really in orbit about α Cen A/B? *Mon. Not. Royal Astro. Soc.*, Vol. 261, 1, L5-L7.

35   Hoag A.A., 1950. A peculiar object in Serpens. *Astronomical Journal.* 55: 170.

fled the scene, but no debris from any collision was found so this does not stand up in court.

Other ring galaxies like this have been seen, but not at such nice angles to us, and they are pretty rare, being only 0.1% of galaxies. In an amazing coincidence, another ring galaxy can be seen inside Hoag's object in the background, much more distant.

Although this galaxy is peculiar it does have one thing in common with all the other galaxies. It has a mass of 300 billion Suns and the ring has a mean radius of about 35 kilo-lightyears which means that the acceleration at its edge is again close to that ubiquitous acceleration: 2×10^{-10} m/s².

5.20 MAGNETARS

Magnetars are thought to be neutron stars that rotate so fast that they are magnets expelling jets, & fast radio bursts, at their poles.

Magnetars were first glimpsed by a satellite in 1979 when a sudden wave of gamma rays passed over the Earth. In 2008 one of these gamma ray deluges was seen to originate at a neutron star. These are stars that have collapsed to such

Figure 21. A magnetar.

an extent that they are simply formed of neutrons crammed together like sardines in a tin. One teaspoon of their matter would weigh the same as a mountain on Earth. How do they produce these intense jets and gamma ray bursts?[36]

The solution, it is thought, is that they (see the schematic above) are spinning so fast and their interiors are so exotic that

---

36   Briggs, A., 2020. What is a Magnetar? Earth Sky.

a massive magnetic field is generated. As we know from sprinkling iron filings around magnets, the magnetic field along which charges migrate allows flow from the poles outwards. Maybe this is the origin of the jets, which are shown above by the white lines, but no-one knows. If the jets are of visible light then what we have is a pulsar: a space lighthouse. The even more mysterious fast radio bursts (FRBs) may also originate from magnetars.

As in sections 5.5 and 5.6, spin axes are interesting. See 7.20 and 7.21.

5.21 KUIPER CLIFF

The Kuiper Belt stops abruptly at a distance of 50 AU. Why?

The Kuiper Belt is an asteroid-belt-like collection of frozen rocks and ice (water, methane and ammonia) from 33 to 55 AU from the Sun (see the mottled ring in the schematic). It is similar to the asteroid belt

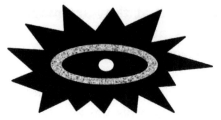

Figure 22. The Kuiper Belt.

between Mars and Jupiter but has 200 times the mass and contains minor planets such as Pluto. The mystery is that the density of material drops abruptly at 55 AU from the Sun and this is called the Kuiper Cliff.[37]

There are two main theories to explain it. Firstly, it could be that the density of objects declines slowly and at some distance it is too low to allow matter to congregate into pieces large enough for us to see (observation bias). However, no-one has used this hypothesis to predict the 55 AUs distance.

---

37   Brooks, M., 2005. 13 Things That Do Not Make Sense. New Scientist.

The second theory is that there is an undetected planet beyond 55 AU that is sweeping space clean from debris (perhaps it should be called Cinderella?) but none has yet been seen, apart from small ones such as Pluto.

Hopefully the New Horizons spacecraft, which is now on a tour of the Kuiper Belt will provide some answers.

5.22 THE SOLAR CORONA

The gaseous envelope surrounding the Sun, its Corona, is more than 200 times hotter than the Sun's surface. Why?

It makes perfect sense that we have developed an aversion to looking directly at the Sun. There is the danger of blindness. Oddly enough, in some ways we have avoided looking at the Sun academically as well. There are several oddities about it: its mass, the fact that the solar wind accelerates, the Sun's possible liquid nature[38] and that fact that the Solar corona is hotter than the Sun itself. The surface of the Sun is 6000K, but the solar corona, the gaseous envelope surrounding it, which can be seen as a bright ring during a solar eclipse, is 200 times hotter than that. Over 1 million Kelvin.

The problem is shown in the schematic. Normally the effect of a source of heat (a gravity-confined fusion explosion in the case of the Sun) reduces as you move away from the source and intense heat (white) cools (grey) (see the left panel). Amazingly (the right panel) the Sun has a surrounding gaseous envelope more than 200 times hotter than the Solar surface.[39] Some other process must be heating the corona, but it is not yet clear what it is.

---

38   Unzicker, A., 2023. The Liquid Sun (a book summarising the liquid Sun theory of Robataille).

39   Crockett, C., 2019. What's hotter than the surface of the Sun? The Solar corona. *Astronomy*. Sept 25th.

Figure 23. The thermal environment of the Sun.

5.23 KUIPER BELT ORBIT ANOMALY

Observed Kuiper Belt objects have orbits that approach the Sun in unison & moving from ecliptic south to north. Strange & unexplained.

In 2014 Trujillo and Shepard[40] noticed that asteroids beyond the orbit of Neptune at 30 AU (Astronomical Units) from the Sun all had a point of closest approach to the Sun (perihelia) in the same region (see Perihelion on the schematic below), and they were all moving from the south of the ecliptic (the flat plane that the planets orbit in) to the north (see the arrow).

The Kuiper belt Objects (KBO) may have formed in the inner Solar system and been kicked out to the edges by encounters with the gas giants but their orbits should be random. It may be possible that we are seeing more of them with perihelia along the ecliptic because they are easier to see (ie closer) but there is no good reason so far why they should all have the same ecliptic longitude which is between 70 and 120 degrees and an orbit that takes them from the south to the north.

One possible reason for this would be if there was a Planet 9 at the position shown on the schematic[41], shepherding the

---

40   Trujillo C.A and S.S. Shepard, 2014. A Sedna-like body with a perihelion of 80 AU. *Nature*, 507, 471.

41   Batygin, K. and M.E. Brown, 2016. Evidence for a distant giant planet in the Solar system. *Astronomical Journal*, 151, 22.

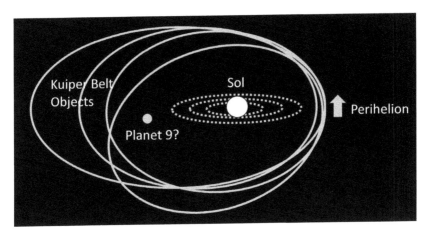

Figure 24. Kuiper belt objects and Planet 9.

KBOs, but no Planet 9 has been found: more oddities in very low acceleration environments.

5.24 THE PIONEER ANOMALY

The Pioneer probes showed a dynamical anomaly–maybe.

The Pioneer 10 and 11 spacecraft were launched in 1972 and 1973 and are now (2023) over 114 AU and 92 AUs away from the Sun respectively. They were spin-stabilised, like rifle bullets. This was done to make sure that tiny asymmetries were made irrelevant by the spin, and the craft then travel in a straight line and do not require so many blasts of the engine. This made their trajectory data cleaner–the first very low acceleration ballistics experiments. In 1998 Anderson et al. noticed a small unexplained acceleration was occurring, directed towards the Sun, of $8.74\pm1.33\times10^{-10}$ m/s^2 known as the Pioneer anomaly[42]. The exponent may seem familiar...

---

42   Anderson, J.D., P.A.Laing, E.L. Lau, A.S. Liu, M.M. Nieto and S.G. Turyshev, 1998. Indication from Pioneer, 10/11, Galileo & Ulysses data of an apparent weak anomalous, long range acceleration. *Phys. Rev. Lett.*, 81, 2858-2861.

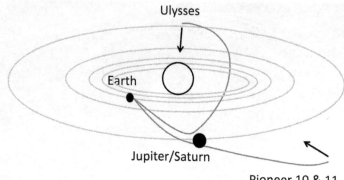

Figure 25. Pioneer 10 and 11 left the Solar system showing an anomalous acceleration towards the Sun (black arrow). The Ulysses probe followed a trajectory over the Sun's pole & showed a similar anomaly (arrow).

Some argue that the Pioneer anomaly is due to radiation bouncing off the radio dish of the craft, but their explanation relies on many assumptions: a model with 2000 finite elements and 2 fitting parameters and it does not explain why a similar anomaly occurred for the Galileo and Ulysses spacecraft which had a different design and trajectory.

5.25 THE FLYBY ANOMALIES

Spacecraft flying by Earth show unexpected changes in speed.

When spacecraft are launched from Earth, they are often designed to have a trajectory that passes behind the Earth in its orbit in such a way that the Earth pulls them along for awhile. This is called a flyby or gravity assist. It was noticed by Anderson et al.[43], that when these spacecraft approach the Earth with a low latitude and leave at a higher latitude they gain unexpected speed. The largest gain recorded was 14 mm/s,

---

43   Anderson, J.D., J.K. Campbell, J.E. Ekelund, J. Ellis, J.F. Jordan, 2008. *Phys. Rev. Lett.*, 100, 091102.

significant given the great accuracy to which they can determine the speed (usually by using the Doppler shift of radio signals, and a radar ranging process).

There have so far been 12 such flybys, most of them showing a nice correlation with latitude, but a recent one, the flyby of Juno, was expected to show an anomaly but didn't, so there is the possibility that something was amiss in the software or geophysical models somewhere and that has now been fixed. Only time will tell.

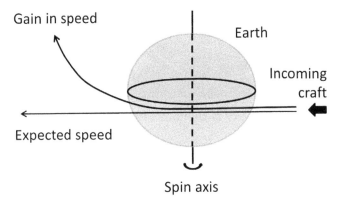

Figure 26. Spacecraft approaching Earth and leaving at an equatorial latitude show no or little anomaly. Spacecraft approaching at the equator and leaving at the pole show a small boost in speed. See also section 7.20.

5.26 OUMUAMUA

An asteroid-like object passing through the Solar system showed a non-gravitational acceleration when moving away from the Sun.

In 2017, the Pan-STARRS survey discovered an asteroid-like object heading away from the Sun with a speed so rapid that it could escape the Solar system. This was taken to mean it was an interstellar object.

Another peculiarity about it was that it was found to be showing a non-gravitational acceleration away from the Sun,

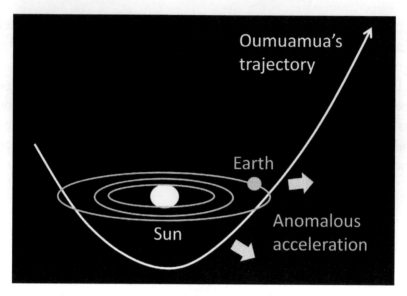

Figure 27. The trajectory of Oumuamua

of $5\pm0.16\times10^{-6}$ m/s^2 at a distance of 1 AU away from the Sun[44]. Analysis of the track showed this acceleration decreased by either $1/r$ or $1/r^2$, where r is the distance from the Sun.

A push from Solar radiation, would account for the $1/r^2$ dependency, but was discounted because it is weak, and to be affected Oumuamua would have to be a flat sail or a low density foam. The possibility that it was a comet being pushed by its own outgassing was discounted: no out-gassing was seen. The anomaly could also be explained if the Sun had temporarily lost 0.1% of its mass (or G varies, which it might, see section 7.22).

It was even suggested that it might be an alien probe.[45] There is no direct evidence for that either, though its sudden acceleration after scanning the Earth might well be taken as evidence of intelligence.

---

44   Micheli, et al., 2018. Non-gravitational acceleration in the trajectory of 1I/2017 U1 'Oumuamua'. *Nature*, 559, 223-226.

45   Loeb, A., 2021. Extraterrestrial: the first sign of intelligent life beyond Earth. HMHBooks.

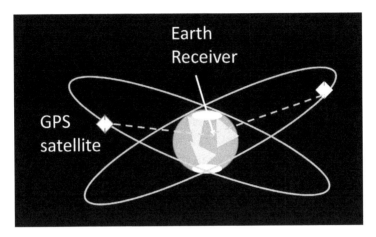

Figure 28. GPS Satellite orbits

5.27 THE GPS ANOMALY

GPS satellites fall too fast.

GPS satellites (see the white diamonds on the schematic) are used to determine our positions on Earth. Each satellite has a very accurate clock on board and sends out a time signal by radio (dashed lines). When a receiver on the Earth (follow the arrow) picks up the signal and compares it with its clock, there is a time delay which tells it its distance from the satellite. If it does the same with more than five GPS satellites then the Earth receiver can triangulate its position on the Earth to a few metres.

In order to do this we need to know accurately the positions of the satellites. This is easy to do since they are orbiting so high up (20,000 km) that friction is low and their orbits can be accurately predicted.

These GPS satellites then, make a great experiment to test standard dynamics at high accuracy. Are they doing what Newton said they should? A careful study[46] pointed out that they are accelerating Earthward a bit more than they should be, by

---

46   Ziebart, M, A. Sibthorpe, P. Cross, Y. Bar-Sever, B. Haines, 2007. Cracking the GPS-SLR orbit anomaly. Proceedings of ION-GNSS-2007, Fort Worth, Session, F-4, p2033-2038.

about 7×10^{-10} m/s^2. Again, you might recognise this exponent. This is close to the acceleration at which galaxies, globular clusters, wide binaries, Hoag's object, Proxima Centauri and maybe space probes start to deviate from the expected behaviour.

Also, if you accelerate at this rate for the age of the cosmos then you end up with the speed of light. The acceleration is also c^2/(Cosmic scale). What is such a cosmic number doing in Earth's orbit? (all will be revealed)

5.28 THE EMDRIVE

Truncated metal cones with microwaves resonating in them, may show a small thrust towards their narrower ends.

Roger Shawyer claimed in 2002 that if microwaves resonate within a truncated conical cavity, then there is tiny thrust towards the narrow end.[47]

This is a severe violation of the principle of conservation of momentum. Normally in nature it is as if there is a momentum accountant who makes sure that momentum (mass times velocity) is conserved. So, if you suddenly find yourself in deep space, with a space suit on and inconveniently far from your comfortable-looking spaceship with an open door, what would you do? Swimming won't help. What you can do is throw something off yourself in the direction away from the spaceship. The momentum

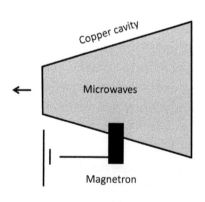

Figure 29. The Emdrive

---

47   Shawer, R., 2008. Microwave propulsion—progress in the emdrive program. 59th IAC-2008, Glasgow, UK.

accountant would then see that that object has taken some momentum away from you, and to keep the overall momentum of the cosmos constant he would give the opposite momentum to you, and you'd move slowly towards the spaceship (more slowly than the object you threw away if that object was lighter).

This principle was explained very well by a recent film 'Interstellar' in which a robot droned 'The only way humans have found for getting anywhere is to leave something behind: Newton's Third Law.' And it means that for example if you are sitting in a car, you can't accelerate it by pushing on the dashboard. To increase speed forward you'd need to eject something backwards (like your sister's shoes for example).

The Emdrive has caused so much consternation because apparently it moves leftwards (in the diagram above) without ejecting anything at all! So, if it is a true effect, then it is the first time humankind has cheated the momentum accountant.

Some have suggested it is possibly a leakage of radiation out of the cavity. The force you get by firing light radiation out of a torch is $F=P/c$ where P is the power and c is the speed of light. Since the speed of light is so large this radiation recoil force is tiny. For the emdrive it is $F=850/3 \times 10^8 = 3\mu N$ whereas the observed thrust was a few mN: one thousand times larger.

NASA's Eagleworks lab reproduced the experiment[48] and also found an anomalous thrust. On the other hand, Martin Tajmar in Germany, famous for disproving new spacedrives, tried it and saw no thrust.[49]

The debate seems to have hardened into the no-thrust camp, possibly due to over-caution, but interested parties are still testing, because the applications, would be game changing for

---

48   White, H., P. March, J. Lawrence, J. Vera, A. Sylvester, D. Brady and P. Bailey, 2017. *J. Propulsion and Power*, 33, 830.

49   Tajmar, M., O. Neunzig and M. Weikert, 2021. CEAS Space Journal, 14, 31-44.

many fields such as transport since it enables thrust without the need to carry heavy, dirty, propellant. We will come back to this in section 7.26.

5.29 HESDALLEN LIGHTS

What causes the mysterious lights at Hesdallen in central Norway?

Norwegians are a pretty sensible bunch, but in 1981 the 150 people in the valley of Hesdallen started reporting strange lights in their sky. Most visible at night of course, the lights were typically small, white or yellow and nothing like the aurora borealis. A typical sighting lasts for a few minutes with a light appearing, splitting and sometimes sucking smaller lights in.

The lights have been seen to be static, moving, singly or in groups. They have also been tracked by radar (which shows they are either solid, or composed of ionised air) at speeds of up to 8000 m/s. In 1983 the frequency of these lights decreased, but they still occur today and a scientific station has been set up to monitor them: The Hesdallen Project.[50]

What is the cause? The valley is in an area famed for metal mines and there is metal dust in the air. One theory claims that the scandium and metal dust is reacting strongly with acids in the air and producing a kind of combustion, so that the light seen is air being turned into a plasma in which electrons are stripped from their atoms. A plasma is detectable to radar.[51]

Another theory points out that one side of the valley the rocks are rich in zinc and iron, on the other side they are rich in copper. This means that the valley is like a battery: one side rich in electrons, the other not, so an electric current may flow.

---

50   Project Hesdallen. http://www.hessdalen.org/

51   Paiva, G.S., C.A. Taft, 2010. A hypothetical dusty plasma mechanism for the Hesdallen lights. *J. Atmos. And Solar-Terrestrial Physics.* 72, 16, 1200-1203.

There is another wild theory that the Hesdallen Lights are an invention of the Norwegian Tourist Board, but there is no evidence for that. By all means, go and look: this anomaly, though rare, can be seen by all.

5.30 WHERE DID ALL THE MUONS GO?

Beauty quarks should decay equally into electrons & muons. Nope!

An experiment at the CERN particle accelerator called the LHCb pays its way by smashing protons into each other and watching as various particles emerge. Protons are thought to contain beauty or bottom quarks and the standard model predicts that these quarks should decay into equal numbers of electrons and muons, which can be called 'fat electrons'. Muons have the same charge as electrons but 207 times the mass.

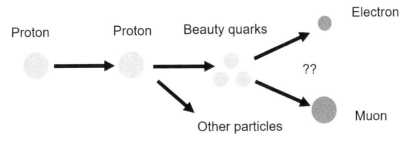

Figure 30. Beauty quark decays.

The LHCb experiment has shown[52] that 15.4% more electrons are formed than muons and this violates the standard model at 3.1 sigma which means that there is only a one in a thousand chance that this is a random fluctuation in the experimental data.

"If a violation of lepton flavour universality were to be confirmed, it would require a new physical process,

52   LHCb Collaboration. Test of lepton universality in beauty-quark decays. *Nature Physics* 18, 277-282.

such as the existence of new fundamental particles or interactions,"

—LHCb spokesperson Professor Chris Parkes
from the University of Manchester and CERN.

The muon is an interesting maverick. It is challenging the standard model in three different experiments, two discussed in this book: the proton radius anomaly, 5.52, the anomalous magnetic moment and this one. Go Muons!

5.31 THE ABRAHAM-MINKOWSKI PARADOX

Physics cannot decide what happens to light's momentum in glass!

Momentum is mass times speed (OK, I know speed is relative and meaningless, but forget about relativity for a minute!). When light passes into water or glass, it slows down. This causes refraction and is the reason why pencils half in water look bent, but what happens to the photons' momentum? Physics, helpfully, says that it goes either up, or down!

Abraham (1909) argued that the momentum (p) reduces in the water or glass, as $p=\hbar\omega/cn$, where n is the refractive index, n=1 in air, n=1.5 in glass, whereas Minkowski (1908) said that it increases, $p=\hbar\omega n/c$. The puzzling situation is shown below. A light beam (the dashed line) enters water or glass (grey block). It slows down (indicated by the closer dashes). It speeds up again upon leaving, but what is its momentum throughout?

She et al.[53] showed that a fibre optic recoils as light leaves it, supporting Abraham: as light comes out of the glass it gains momentum, so the cosmic accountant moves the glass back-

---

53   She, J., Yu., Feng, 2008. Observation of a push force on the end face of a nanometer silica filament exerted by outgoing light. *Phys. Rev. Lett.* 101 (24): 243601.

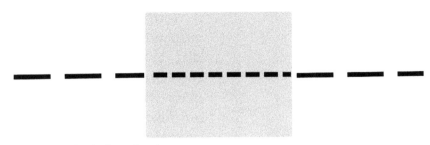

Figure 31. Light slows in glass.

wards to compensate. On the other hand Campbell et al.[54] showed that the recoil momentum of a dilute gas of atoms when impacted by light supports the Minkowski momentum. What interpretation is correct? To find out we may need a better understanding of what light is. Paradoxes are useful in science, they usually indicate to us a deep misunderstanding. The solution to this one may involve considering the momentum carried by the atoms in the glass.

5.32 THE PODKLETNOV EFFECT

Do superconductors shield objects from gravity?

In the 1990s, Dr Yevgeny Podkletnov was working in Finland at Tampere University on superconducting (SC) discs. His team were levitating such a disc (see the grey rectangles below) using the Meissner effect due to which SCs rise up over permanent magnets (the black rectangles in the schematic). This disc had the unique characteristic of having a finer grain size on top than on the bottom (shown by the mottling effect).

Luckily, global neuroticism had not yet taken over, and one of the team was smoking. They noticed that the smoke was rising over the disc, the black trails in the schematic.

---

54 Campbell, G.K., A. E. Leonhardt, J. Mun, M. Boyd, E. W. Streed, W. Ketterle; D. E. Pritchard, 2005. Photon recoil momentum in dispersive media. *Physical Review Letters*. 94 (17).

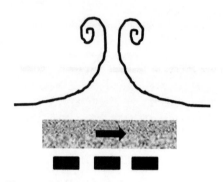

Figure 32. Air rising over a spinning superconductor.

Noticing this, they tried suspending objects over the disc and they found that they lost 0.05% of their mass. This was not due to air flow or buoyancy effects because it persisted when they were encased in glass. It was not due to magnetic effects because it persisted when a metal sheet was placed between the disc and the object. The effect increased towards the edge of the disc, and when the discs were spun at about 3000 rpm or accelerated, the weight loss increased to about 0.5%. When Podkletnov published his findings in 1992[55] a furore occurred that got him fired. He had to move back to Russia. The controversial result was hotly debated, but no team has yet succeeded in reproducing the exact circumstance of the test.

5.33 THE BLACK HOLE INFORMATION PARADOX

Is information lost in black holes or not?

Strictly this is not an anomaly, but is interesting in light of the theory presented later in this book. If matter congregates to a sufficiently high density, then the gravitational pull it exerts is so strong that light cannot escape. From outside, it is a black hole surrounded by an event horizon.

In 1976 Hawking looked at what black holes do for virtual particles that always form in pairs. He showed that the event

---

55   Podkletnov, E.E. Nieminen, R., 1992. A possibility of gravitational shielding by bulk YBa2Cu3O7-x superconductor, *Physica C*, 203, 441-444.

Figure 33. A black hole swallowing information.

horizon separates them so they cannot recombine, and the one outside the hole becomes real and is emitted as Hawking radiation[56]. This means that whereas black holes can hoover up information-full objects such as flowers and manuscripts (see left), they can only emit thermal, random, Hawking radiation.

Hawking, Kip Thorne and Roger Penrose were perfectly happy to have information destroyed but Leonard Susskind and Gerard t'Hooft published a book called The Black Hole War saying that Hawking was violating one of the laws of the universe: the conservation of information. Since when has that been a law? They suggested that the information that goes into the black hole is stored in its horizon. Hawking, oddly, conceded he had lost.

The debate is at the heart of physics, which has still not come to grips with information. Landauer's principle argues that when computer memory is erased this is a reduction of information and entropy, which cannot be allowed, so heat must be released. What is this but a loss of information?

---

56   Hawking, S., 1975. Particle creation by black holes. *Comm. Math. Phys.*, 43, 199-220.

5.34 LIGHT FROM NANOCAVITIES

When a tungsten photonic crystal is heated, it emits about eight times as much light as expected from Planck's law. It cannot be? Oh, it be!

It is well known and verified that all bodies radiate according to Planck's law. The power (P) emitted is $P = \sigma T^4$ where σ is the Stefan-Boltzmann constant (5.67×10^{-8} Wm^{-2}K^{-4}) and T is the absolute temperature in Kelvin. This is a strict limit. Nothing has ever been observed to radiate more than this. So why then is it that Shawn-Yu Lin built a Si/SiO$_2$ cavity above a tungsten photonic crystal[57], made of a 1-d grid of tungsten rods (see schematic below, rod length into the page), heated it from below (see the box) and saw eight times as much light coming off as Plank predicted given its temperature?[58]

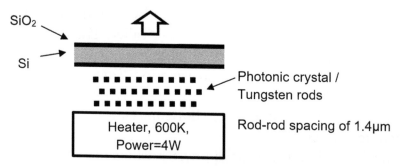

Figure 34. A photonic crystal emitting unexpected heat.

The radiation emitted had a peak wavelength of 1.7 μm. This wavelength is suspiciously close to the separation between the tungsten rods in the photonic crystal. Could it be that the light

57 A photonic crystal is a array of dielectric structures that allow only some wavelengths of light to form.

58 Shawy-Yu Lin, 2020. An in-situ and direct Confirmation of Super-Planckian Thermal Radiation Emitted from a Metallic Photonic-Crystal at Optical Wavelengths. *Scientific Reports*, 10, Art. Number 5209.

was formed within those crystals? Could be! See section 7.37 and 7.38 on light in nanocavities and bubbles.

5.35 RANCOURT'S LIGHT BOX

Mass is attracted by light? Gravity is a pushing force?

In standard physics, gravity is a pull from one mass onto another, but what is the mechanism of gravity? General relativity says it is a curvature of spacetime, but what is spacetime? Ernst Mach would not have liked this concept because there is no way to directly test it, other than using the observation it was designed to explain (tracking the bodies' motion).

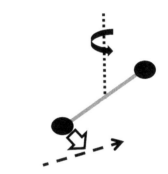

Newton's colleague de Fatio, Le Sage, and also Phoebe on the sit-com Friends ('The One Where Heckles Dies'), suggested that gravity may be a

Figure 35. Is a suspended torsion balance attracted to light?.

pushing force. This flies in the face of educated opinion, but around 2011 a Canadian teacher called Louis Rancourt, set up the following experiment.

Two masses (black balls), at either end of a solid bar (gray line) hang on a thin wire (dotted line). A laser is fired past one of the balls (dashed arrow). Rancourt found that the ball moved towards the light.[59] Further, a light box placed over a mass decreased its weight by 0.036%. Rancourt suggested this means that gravity is caused by particles that are zipping through the air hitting matter from all directions and the laser is blocking

---

59   Rancourt, L.J., 2011. Effect of light on gravitational attraction. *Physics Essays*. 24(4), 557-

them from one direction causing the particles from the other direction to push the object towards the laser. Could this be due to Unruh radiation? (see later). We should be a little cautious about these experiments as the delay seen could suggest a thermal cause, unless the delay is a plasma being formed.

5.36 THE DARK RATE

When you heat a metal more electrons escape because there is more energy available. Oddly, more escape when it cools way down as well.

When light shines on a metal, the energy in the light allows electrons to jump out of the metal, as shown here. This is called the photoelectric effect and Einstein won his Nobel prize for explaining peculiarities of it in 1905.

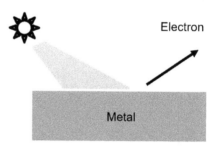

Figure 36. The photoelectric effect.

Electrons in this sense are a little like human beings who need a little sunlight or energy to get out of bed. Another way to get humans out of a bed would be to put the bed in liquid nitrogen. Keep that thought!

Around 2010 Hans-Otto Meyer was looking at photoelectric emission from photomultiplier cathodes and he found that indeed if you warm a metal above 0°C then electron emission increases, but bizarrely if you cool the metal below 0°C all the way down to 4K (-269°C), then the emission of electrons also increases, and it increases linearly and electrons are emitted in bursts. With lower temperatures the bursts become more frequent and longer.[60] This is a well-known problem in pho-

---

60   Meyer, H.O, 2010. Spontaneous electron emission from a cold surface. *EPL*, 89, 58001.

tomultipliers which rely on the photoelectric effect to detect photons. They have long been known to have a dark rate—they detect photons even in the dark, due to this process. At the moment, physics cannot explain this.

5.37 BALL LIGHTNING

Centuries of personal or group accounts, lab tests and one recent observation show balls of light form & float above the ground.

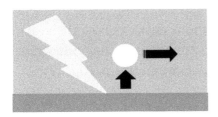

Figure 37. The formation of ball lightning.

In 1638 a great ball of light came through a stained glass window during a thunderstorm, and must have hugely impressed the worshippers present. Presumably their God-fearing behaviour was excellent the following week! Since then, there have been many accounts of ball lightening—balls of intense light that float above the ground, move sideways, make a hissing sound, have an acrid odour and occur often during thunderstorms and, perhaps, earthquakes as well.

In one explanation, suggested by Abrahamson, lightning strikes the ground (see the schematic), vaporising Silicon Oxide and carbon in the soil. The Carbon steals the Oxygen from the Silicon which gets it back from the atmosphere, by burning. In 2012, Chinese scientists filmed ball lightning and took a spectrograph to determine the elements in it. It turned out to be 'lit soil', as in the Abrahamson theory—the elements determined from the wavelengths in the spectrograph were the same as those in the local soil, but there are still unresolved issues.[61]

Other theories are that ball lightning induces a brain-storm with the ball being an illusion, or that they are magnetically trapped balls of plasma. See also section 7.33.

5.38 EPR-BELL ANOMALY

Quantum particles can communicate faster than light.

This all began with a paper from Einstein, Podolski and Rosen (EPR) in 1935[62]. Imagine you have the pair production of two particles A and B at a point in space & they fly apart, one spinning up and one down. You let them separate by light years and then measure the spin of A. It's up, so the other one must be spinning down to conserve angular momentum. Right?

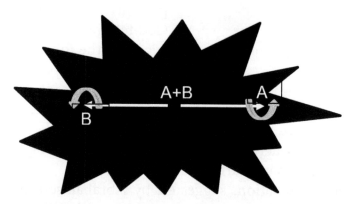

Figure 38. Particles A & B, after separation.

The trouble, pointed out in this 1935 paper is that the spin is not encoded in the quantum wavefunction, so either there are some

---

61   Nunez, C., 2019. Ball lightning: weird, mysterious perplexing & deadly. *National Geographic*. March 5th.

62   Einstein, A., Podolsky, B., Rosen, N., 1935. Can Quantum-Mechanical Description of Physical Reality Be Considered Complete? *Physical Review*. 47 (10): 777–780.

'hidden variables' stored in the wavefunction (rewriting quantum mechanics) or particle B can instantly communicate with particle A to tell it its spin when measured (rewrite relativity). This ignores the fact that WE cannot know particle B is spin-down because to do so we'd need to travel there and WE are limited to light speed. So this is a nice thought experiment, but untestable.

It was made testable by John Bell in 1964. He showed that if you do this experiment in a lab, there is a way to get a difference in the result depending on whether hidden variables or faster than light signalling are going on. The experiment was first done by Alain Aspect[63] and the result, and others, show that the weird faster than light assumption is correct.

5.39 THE HARTMAN EFFECT.

When quantum particles approach a barrier, there's a small chance that they'll pass through at speeds faster than light.

When quantum mechanics was first proposed it was quickly realised that it predicted some odd things. For example, if a ball approaches a brick wall in classical physics, then it always bounces back, but in quantum mechanics there is a tiny chance that the object will pass through the wall.

This was measured and is called 'quantum tunnelling'. In 1962 Thomas Hartman[64] found that when particles do pass through the barrier, they travel faster than light. This is now called the Hartman effect. Scientists have used the precession of the spin of particles to work out how long they take to go

---

63   Aspect, A., 1999. Bell's inequality test: more real than ever. *Nature*, Vol. 398. 189-190.

64   Hartman, T.E., 1962. Tunneling of a Wave Packet. *Journal of Applied Physics*, 33, 3427

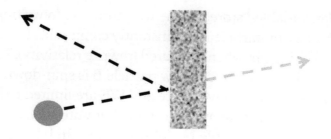

Figure 39. A ball bounces off a wall, or does it?

through the barrier and speeds of up to 4.7c have been measured this way[65]. A debate continues over whether what is being seen is simply a boost occurring because the wave of the particle is shifting its peak to the front, and 'cheating'.

The uses of this are obvious. For example, you could send a signal faster than light, but the problem is that although they do beat light speed inside the barrier the chance of a particle passing through is so small that you'd have to expend a lot of energy to get a decent amount of information through. Maybe a postal quantum surcharge is in the future?

5.40 NEUTRON LIFETIME ANOMALY,

Neutrons decay to protons outside the atom, but neutrons moving in beams last 9 seconds (~1%) longer than those static in bottles.

There are two ways to measure the lifetime of neutrons. The first way is to put the neutrons (the light grey dots in the left hand image below) in a box and count how many remain as neutrons after a particular time. That experiment leads to a mean lifetime of 879.3±0.75 seconds. The other way is to fire a beam

---

65   Ramos, R., D. Spierlings, I. Racicot, A.M. Steinberg, 2020. *Nature*, 583, 529-532.

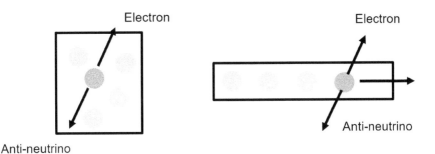

Figure 40. Neutron decay, static or moving.

of neutrons down a pipe (the right hand image) and count the number that come out. In this case they last 888±2.1 seconds.

This problem was first noticed by Serebrov and his team[66]. The difficulty here is that the two experiments both claim to be absolutely sure of their value within one or two seconds, see the uncertainties (±s), but they obviously differ by more than that! This means there's something funny going on. It's like two boys swearing they saw UFOs, but one is adamant he saw 3 and the other is sure he saw only one. What would Mulder do? It means another variable is in play. Maybe one of the boys saw the UFOs from an angle and they are in line. What's the extra factor regarding this experiment, or is experimental physics just going down the tubes?

5.41 THE ALLAIS EFFECT

During Solar eclipses, swinging pendulums suddenly rotate their plane of swing forward, and then back at the end of the eclipse.

Pendulums are fascinating. When swinging, like gyroscopes, they like to stay in the same orientation in absolute space, so

---

66   Serebrov, A. et al., 2005. *Physics Letters B*, Volume 605, Issue 1-2, p. 72-78.

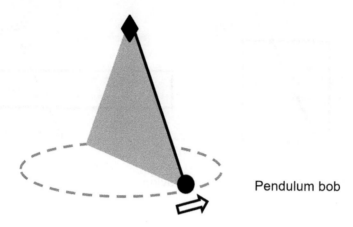

Figure 41. The rotation of a pendulum's swing.

as the Earth spins below them, their plane of swing appears to us to slowly rotate clockwise as looked at from above. This is because, in the northern hemisphere, the Earth spins anti-clockwise. We are turning, not the pendulum. At the pole the pendulum would rotate once per day, but at mid latitudes it turns slower.

Maurice Allais (Nobel prize in economics, 1988) noticed during experiments in 1954–though God knows what made him try this–that during Solar eclipses the plane of the pendulum's swing moves forwards faster than expected. It shifts clockwise by about 10 degrees and at the end of the eclipse it shifts back.[67] This gave him quite a turn, and wider physics as well which has so far not come up with an explanation.

The fact that it is a twisting, points to some sort of intrinsic change to the mass of the pendulum. Something fundamental...

---

67   The Economist, 2004. An Invisible Hand? Aug 19th.

5.42 THE POHER EFFECT

When a capacitor is discharged through a layered super-conducting ceramic, the ceramic moves up & objects below it move down.

Claude Poher is an empirical scientist of the old school, and French. When I emailed him to ask about his experiment his reply began with "Young man..." which tells you something about what was to follow. An admonition that one should do all one's experiments oneself.

The experiment he performed was difficult.[68] He charged up a capacitor (on the left below) to a voltage of between 0 and 4000V and then discharged it through a layered ceramic, one layer of which (denoted SC) was superconducting at 70K (the whole device was in liquid Nitrogen, the light grey shading) as shown below

The result was a force upwards on the ceramic (the upwards arrow) opposite in direction to the electron flow, and a force downwards on objects and accelerometers placed below the ceramic. Also observed were a whiplash-like sound and flashes

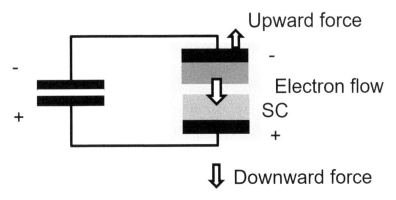

Figure 42. The Poher Effect.

68   Poher, C., D. Poher and P. Marquet, 2010. Propelling phenomenon revealed by electric discharges into layered Y123 superconducting ceramics. *Eur. Phys. J. Appl. Phys.*, 50, 30803 (suspended)

of light similar to nitrogen emission lines from below the ceramic. Whatever was causing the downwards force, made small waves in water placed below. In a strange move, after being peer-reviewed, accepted and published, Poher's paper was retracted by the journal shortly after.

5.43 ASYMMETRIC CAPACITOR THRUST

When a capacitor discharges through a dielectric there may be an unexplained force on the capacitor towards the anode.

T.T. Brown was a talented but controversial figure. He performed experiments that seemed to show that capacitors (two close parallel metal plates that are used to store electrical energy) when discharged, often moved towards their anodes,

Figure 43. An asymmetrical capacitor with dielectric.

the positive terminal towards which the electrons move during a discharge. In 2004 NASA published a paper arguing similarly[69]. They had a copper capacitor with the anode on the left and the cathode on the right and a dielectric in the centre (the grey area).

They placed the capacitor in a vacuum and the voltage between the two electrodes was increased to 44kV and then "Something interesting happened". They observed the flash of a large arc towards the anode, and the capacitor moved towards the anode with a force of about 0.014 Newtons. At first they thought this movement was simply a response from Newton's

---

69   Canning F.X., C. Melcher & E. Winet, 2004. Asymmetric capacitors for propulsion. NASA/CR-2004-213312.

third law, a recoil from the material lost from the electrodes upon sparking, but they managed to repeat this thrust several times over a period of an hour and if this was material loss they would have used up ten times the material in the cylinder and in fact no degradation of the cathode or anode was seen. There is a nice summary of these experiments here[70].

5.44 HAYASAKA'S FALLING SPINNERS.

Discs fall slower if they are spinning clockwise as seen from above, as if g was 0.1% smaller, but an anticlockwise spin has no effect.

Hideo Hayasaka performed experiments in 1997 in which he dropped gyroscopes in a vacuum tower (see the black boxes below) and used lasers to time their fall over a known height (see the grey lines—the laser trip wires). He dropped them without spin and then spinning anticlockwise (see the arrows in the left panel) and clockwise (see the right panel), compared the fall-time, and calculated the gravitational acceleration.

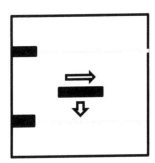 

Figure 44.
Spinners falling
under gravity.

70   Martins, A.A. and M.J. Pinheiro, 2011. On the propulsive force develop by asymmetric capacitors in a vacuum. SPESIF-2011. Physics Procedia, 20, 112-119.

The result was that the discs that were spinning in an anti-clockwise sense looking on from above (the left panel) fell more slowly than those spinning in a clockwise sense looking from above (the right panel). For a spin of 18,000 rpm for a 5.8 cm diameter disc the apparent difference in the gravitational acceleration was 0.14±0.03gal or 0.0014 m/s². In previous work they also showed that the right spinning induced a decrease of weight proportional to the rate of spin.[71]

As usual, a mundane error cannot be ruled out, but none have been shown to agree with this behaviour so far. There is no explanation for this behaviour in standard physics. Accelerations should not depend on rotation rates, or directions, so Newton must be spinning in his grave.

5.45 THE FINE STRUCTURE CONSTANT

The ratio between the speed of the electron in its orbit and the speed of light is 137.04. Where does this bizarre number come from?

What is the fine structure constant? If you consider two particles of a Planck mass (about 2.18×10^{-8} kg) and the elementary charge (charge on the electron) then the fine structure constant (denoted as α) is the ratio between the gravitational force of attraction to the electrostatic repulsion. As said above, it is also the ratio between the orbital speed of the electron and the speed of light. Its value is given by $\alpha = e^2 / 4\pi\varepsilon_0 \hbar c$ where e is the charge on the electron, ε_0 is the permittivity of free space, $\hbar$ is the reduced Planck constant and c is the speed of light. Richard Feynman declared α to be "One of the great damn mysteries of physics".

---

71   Hayasaka, H., et al., 1997. Possibility for the existence of anti-gravity: evidence from a freefall experiment using a spinning gyro. *Speculations in Science and Technology*, 20, 173-181.

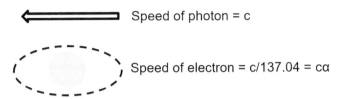

Figure 45. One meaning of the fine structure constant, α.

When you calculate α using the formula above, then the units all cancel out, so that this number is dimensionless, like Pi, and so it does not matter which system of units we use (Imperial, Metric, SI) the value is always the same and it would be also for an alien civilisation with their system of units.

Observed variations in the fine structure constant with space and time will be dealt with elsewhere but the first amazing thing about it is simply its value. Why 1/137.04? Why not 1/42 for example? No-one knows.[72] Is it fundamental or does it just emerge by chance?

5.46 ACOUSTIC ALCHEMY

Iron bars subjected to ultrasound emitted neutrons & showed patches where iron disappeared & carbon & oxygen appeared. Nuclear Fission?

Cardone et al. set up an iron bar and used what they called a sonotrobe, a vibrator, to apply ultrasound to it at a frequency of 20 kHz and a power of 19W as shown below. There was a reflector below the bar to keep the sound inside the metal bar.

The first surprise they got was that, after 40 minutes, bursts of neutrons were emitted, up to 25% above the background level. This was not a huge flux but was thought to be significant. This is a sign that nuclear reactions are taking place, since neutrons are only found in the nucleus. This is similar to the claims

---

72   Unzicker, A., 2014. Einstein's Lost Key.

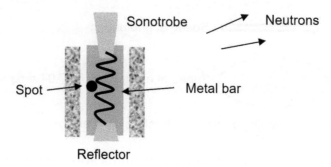

Figure 46. An iron bar subject to ultrasound emits neutrons.

for cold fusion. The second surprise was that afterwards the bars all had spots on them 2-3 mm wide, in which apparently the iron had been converted into carbon and oxygen.[73]

This is not predicted by any standard physics. Sound is not supposed to have the power to split the atom. One very good use for this mechanism, if it can be confirmed, would be its ability to take heavy radioactive elements and change them into lighter and non-radioactive ones.

Chalk it down to the curative power of music!

5.47 THE GRAVITATIONAL 'CONSTANT'.

The gravitational constant G isn't constant. It has varied by 0.1% over 30 years of measurements. More than the error in the experiments!

Nothing stands on a higher plane than Newton's law of gravity. It has always appeared as if written in stone. It states that the force of gravity is equal to $F=GMm/r^2$ where G is the gravitational constant, $6.67 \times 10^{-11} m^3 kg^{-1} s^{-2}$, M is the central mass (eg the Sun), m is the mass being forced (eg a planet) and r is the distance between them. Over the years G has been measured in

---

73   Cardone, F., R. Mignani, M. Monti, A. Petrucci and V. Sala, 2012. Piezonuclear neutrons from Iron. *Modern Physics Letters A.*, 27, 18, 1250102.

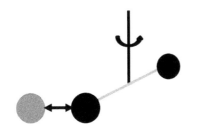

Figure 47. A torsion balance, used to measure G.

the lab with increasing accuracy using Torsion balances:

Two metal balls, or masses (black balls) are joined by a rigid cross bar (grey line) suspended from a wire (black). A test mass (grey ball) is brought close to one of the masses and the force exerted can be measured by the twist in the wire which has a known torsion constant. Thus we can measure F and using Newton's equation, since we know M, m and r we can infer G.

The trouble is that many tests like this have been done and quote small uncertainties, yet the values of G they have measured vary far more than these errors, by 0.1%, suggesting that G depends on something we do not yet know about. G may also vary with a six year period as found by Anderson et al.[74] (see also section 5.26 on Oumuamua).

It looks like the gravitational constant is not a constant at all, which makes it far more interesting, and possibly controllable.

5.48 THE DYNAMICAL CASIMIR EFFECT

You can make photons out of 'nothing'.

The Casimir effect occurs when metal plates are placed microns apart. The quantum vacuum can be thought of as waves, like a sea. When you put two ships together there are fewer waves between them as only waves with a node (non-moving part) on the ship's hull survive friction, so the ships

74   Anderson, J.D, G. Schubert, V. Trimble and M.R. Feldman, 2015. Measurements of Newton's gravitational constant and the length of day. *EPL*, 110, 10002.

get pushed together by the excess of waves hitting them from outside. When you put two metal plates together there are fewer quantum waves between them—the plates force a node as electrons move in the metal to cancel the field, disallowing wavelengths that do not fit. So the plates are pushed together by the excess of quantum waves outside. This effect was measured in 1997 and is illustrated below on the left

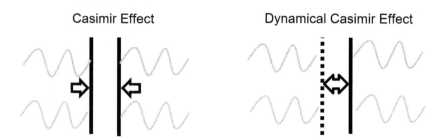

Figure 48. The static and dynamic Casimir effect.

Just as the Casimir effect makes a void in the void that sucks the plates together, so we can do the same by vibrating a mirror close to the speed of light. The quantum waves again need to have a node on the mirror, but the mirror (metal) is moving. It is as if the mirror (see the right hand image) is oscillating between the two positions shown, so it is like the Casimir effect. The problem is that it is difficult to vibrate mirrors this fast without breaking them. Wilson et al.[75] achieved the same effect by varying the impedance of a superconducting quantum interference device which produces an effective mirror. They saw photons emitted from the vacuum, from nothing!

---

75   Wilson, C.M., G. Johansson, A. Pourkabirian, M. Simoen, J.R. Johansson, T. Duty, F. Nori and P. Delsing, 2011. Observation of the dynamical Casimir effect in a superconducting circuit. Nature, 479, 376.

5.49 PUGACH-OLENICI-ALLAIS EFFECT

During a Solar eclipse in India, torsion balances in Ukraine and Romania turned clockwise (seen from above) and then turned back.

Foucault pendulums left to swing, or torsion balances tend to turn slowly clockwise (seen from above in the northern hemisphere) because the Earth is turning anticlockwise below them and they are dutifully trying to stay inertially bound to absolute space. Maurice Allais noticed in 1957 that Foucault pendulums during Solar eclipses tend to turn their plane of rotation clockwise (seen from above), by about 10 degrees. Observations of this have been made since, but not consistently (section 5.41). In 2012 Pugach and Olenici from Ukraine and Romania decided to measure the behaviour of two torsion balances during a Solar eclipse that was happening miles away in India. Their setup is shown below.

Figure 49. Torsion balances twist during an eclipse.

When the eclipse began, sure enough, the torsion balances moved about 10 degrees clockwise (seen from above) and at the end of the eclipse several hours later they slowly moved back. The two torsion balances showed behaviour that was correlated, but offset by about two hours—they were in different places (Kiev and Suceava) leading the authors to conclude that some sort of moving wave was affecting them.[76]

5.50 DELAYED CHOICE EXPERIMENT

In the 2-slit experiment, whether photons chose to go through one or two slits depends on whether we measure them at a later time!

In Young's two-slot experiment, photons are fired from a laser (see the grey box on the left) at a screen with two slits (centre). The photons behave like water waves passing through the slits. Let's place a detector-screen (thick black line on the right) behind the slits to measure where photons hit. If only one slit is open we'd see a single peak on the detector screen (the dark grey curve). If both slits are open, quantum mechanics & experiment show that each photon goes through both slits & the peaks and troughs of its quantum waves interfere so that on a screen we see peaks and troughs (the light grey curve).

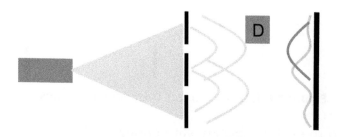

Figure 50. The delayed-choice two-slit experiment.

76   Pugach, A.F., and D. Olenici, 2012. Observations of correlated behaviour of two light torsion balances and a paraconical pendulum in separate locations during the Solar eclipse of January 26th, 2009. *Advances in Astronomy*, Vol. 2012, Art. ID: 263818.

In the delayed choice experiment a detector (D) is placed that only decides whether to measure which slit the photons have passed through after they have passed through the slits. If the detector D is on, it forces the photons to only pass through one slit, but by an action that occurs after the photon has passed through. If the photon is detected after it passed through the slits and therefore the slit it passed through is known, then the pattern on the screen is the one-slit pattern with one peak. If the detector stays off, the pattern is the interference pattern. Therefore, what is apparently happening here is that the detector's action is reaching backwards in time. As for the EPR paradox in section 5.38, photons have absolutely no sense of time.[77]

5.51 THE GLASS BATTERY

Batteries work with two plates of different metals, eg: zinc and copper. A new glass battery works with identical metal plates, but how?

A battery works as in the diagram below. There is a cathode on the left hand side which is made of a metal such as nickel and an anode on the right hand side which can be made of, for example, zinc. They are separated by an electrolyte which contains ions: atoms with charge. Zinc is more electro-negative than nickel, which means that it attracts electrons more, so normally, electrons build up on the anode until it becomes negative enough to stop the process by repelling electrons. If you connect the two electrodes to an external circuit, the electrons flow through the circuit and back to the cathode, the anode is not now negative and starts attracting electrons again and a current continues to flow.

---

77   Vincent, J., et al., 2007. Experimental Realization of Wheeler's Delayed-Choice Gedanken Experiment. *Science*, Vol. 315, Issue 5814, pp. 966-968.

One of the problems with this kind of battery is that solid protuberances called dendrites (black spike) grow out of the cathode, through the liquid electrolyte and when they touch the anode, a spark occurs. Mobile phones

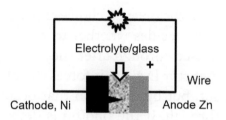

Figure 51. The glass battery.

sometimes catch fire this way. Goodenough and Braga[78] claim to have solved this problem using solid glass instead of a liquid electrolyte. This new battery also lasts much longer, even as metal from the cathode becomes embedded on the anode. The battery should not work under these conditions. However it works, and that's *good enough* for now.

5.52 THE PROTON RADIUS PROBLEM

The proton is the basis of every atom in nature, yet the standard model cannot even predict its radius correctly.

The proton is at the core of physics, being one of the two particles that make up the atomic nucleus. It has a positive charge that balances the negative charge of the electron. Experiments have been done that fire lasers at electrons orbiting the nucleus, forcing them to jump to an outer orbit then decay again to a lower (the dashed circles in the schematic). The size of the jump is affected by the Lamb shift: an inwards force due to sheltering of the zero-point field (shown in grey in the picture—the white areas are sheltered). This sheltering depends on the proton's radius (central ball). So, from the light emitted by the electron as

---

78   Braga, M.H.; M.S. Chandrasekar; A.J., Murchison, J,B. Goodenough, 2018. Nontraditional, Safe, High Voltage Rechargeable Cells of Long Cycle Life. *Journal of the American Chemical Society*. 140 (20), 6343–6352.

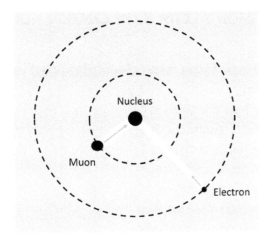

Figure 52. Atomic orbitals of the electron & muon.

it falls back you can infer the proton's radius to be 0.876×10^{-15} metres with a 1% error.

In 2010 a bold group decided to measure the proton's radius, replacing the orbiting electron with a muon, which is 200 times heavier and orbits closer in (see schematic), so that the sheltering effect of the proton would be larger and the determination of its radius from the Lamb shift would be more accurate. The new radius they measured was 0.84×10^{-15} metres. This is 4% smaller, and the uncertainty on the original measurement was only 1%. Oops!

This would be a significant discovery[79] affecting all of physics, and the standard model, since protons are as basic to physics as bread or rice are to a typical diet. It could be explained if the zero point field were enhanced somehow, but that is a story for the latter part of this book.

---

79   Pohl, R. et al., 2010. The size of the proton. *Nature*, 466, 213.

5.53 COLD FUSION / LENR (LOW ENERGY NUCLEAR REACTIONS)

Unexpected heat from the electrolysis of heavy water with palladium.

Fusion is the process by which two atomic nucleii combine. Since nucleii are charged positively, they repel and to join they have to collide pretty fast. It is only supposed to happen at temperatures of 1 million Kelvin, as in the Sun—a reaction that provides most of our heat. To reproduce hot fusion huge reactors are being built at the cost of billions. So imagine the shock when in 1989 Martin Fleischmann and Stanley Pons claimed they had created fusion in a little test tube as shown here.

They put a platinum anode and a palladium cathode into heavy water (D_2O) and electro-

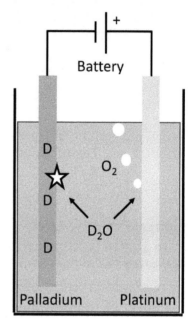

Figure 53. Fusion in a test tube?

lysed it. As expected the D_2O molecule split up into oxygen O (negative charge) which was attracted to the anode and deuterium D (positive) which migrated to the cathode. Palladium can soak up deuterium like a sponge and so it did for a few weeks. Then, oddly the temperature of the water rose from 30°C to 40°C. The heat required was greater than the energy they were putting in electrically, and greater than the chemical energy available as well. Fleischmann & Pons concluded that the only process that could explain it was fusion.[80] The amazement that this announcement generated was short lived. The process is a difficult one to reproduce and critics also pointed out that, if this was fusion, then why weren't gamma rays and neutrons coming off the palladium in amounts guaranteed to fry an ox? Soon cold fusion was out of favour, but an army of brave experimenters and theorists continue to study it. Today there have been 200 or so replications of the effect in labs all around the world. So *something* odd is going on, but what?

5.54 PAIR PRODUCTION

If you tune radio waves to 2.5×10^{20} Hz, near a heavy nucleus, then you can make an electron-positron pair appear out of nothing.

If you tune a radio transmitter slowly through the spectrum towards higher and higher frequency you will be perfectly bored, until suddenly at a frequency of 2.5×10^{20} Hz out will pop an electron and positron, moving off in opposite directions. This

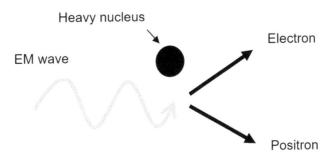

Figure 54. The process of pair production.

---

80   Fleischmann, M. Pons, S., 1989. Electrochemically induced nuclear fusion of deuterium. *Journal of Electroanalytical Chemistry*, 261 (2A): 301–308.

is called pair production, and it also needs a catalyst—a nearby heavy nucleus to absorb access momentum.

Why the frequency of 2.5×10^{20} Hz? Yes, you might say that the equation for energy is E=hf (Energy = Planck's constant times frequency) and the frequency is simply that needed to give us the mass-energy of the electron, but then, why does the electron have the mass-energy it does? How do pure electromagnetic waves, or photons, make solid electrons and positrons? Are these particles then somehow made of photons? Perhaps trapped? By what?[81] Read on...!

---

81   Jennison, R.C., 1979. What is an electron? A new model: the phase locked cavity. *Wireless World*. June 1979.

CHAPTER 6
THE NEW MODEL

6.1 BEGINNINGS

As we have seen, there are now a large number of anomalies (54 listed above) that standard physics does not predict. Amounting, in one sense, to 96% of the cosmos. What is the factor that links them? One factor is that many of them occur at the very low accelerations in deep space, and the others occur at higher accelerations but involve some sort of metal cavity.

In my opinion it is time to rethink the basics, but include from the start the relatively new idea of information to see if the resulting physics is better.

To do this, in this section I will consider one 'thing' by itself in an empty cosmos. Not a particle or a wave, which are the two concepts humanity has been alternating between for hundreds of years, but rather something that has only three abilities: it can emit light, observe light and remember (this is where the information comes in). So let's call it a firefly (like an atom, the smallest unit, indivisible, but including memory or information).

All alone in the empty cosmos this firefly has nothing to see, so it has no way to measure time or space. You could say it has

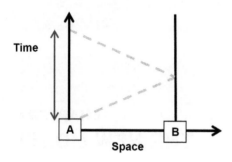

Figure 55. Firefly A emits a light beam (the dashed line) which strikes firefly B and is re-emitted back to A.

no information. It can't even contemplate its own navel because it is dimensionless.

Now if we suddenly put another firefly in there next to it, everything changes. Firefly A (see the space-time schematic) sends out a signal, the dashed line, which bounces off, or is re-emitted by, firefly B, and returns:

In this diagram firefly A is on the left and B is on the right. The x dimension of space is shown horizontally and time is shown vertically. Firefly A sends a signal to B, at the speed of light and makes the lower dashed diagonal line. Then B replies at the speed of light making the upper diagonal line as the signal returns to A. As soon as the signal is received by A, then A can record it, say, by counting and remembering which number it has counted to. Now A sends another signal out, which also comes back and then he can count '2' and A is now aware of time having passed. Until the signals come back A has no way of knowing that time is passing, so using the philosophy of Mach (if you can't measure it, then it doesn't exist) we can say that time does not exist except when A can count. Therefore the time interval between A's emission and reception of the light does not so much represent the time elapsed for A, but the time 'stepped over' by A, or the time erased (T⁻). This can be calculated by the formula

$$T^- = 2x/c$$

Where c is the speed of light and 'x' is the distance from A to B. If A and B now move apart, the time taken for the signal to go between them at the speed of light is longer, and so they step over more time, and count less rapidly and so you could say they age less rapidly. Just as for time dilation in special relativity (also inspired by the philosophy of Mach) this should be a real effect, since if you can't measure time, then it does not exist.

But there is now a problem, because since their perception of time is determined by the distance between them, which is x, the two fireflys can never work out either what the time T actually is, or what the distance x actually is because 1) the two things are not independent and 2) they can't measure intervals of time smaller than T or distances less than x. The only way they can start to do this is to bring in a third firefly, C:

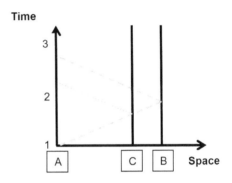

Figure 56. Three fireflys, called A, B and C, exchange light beams.

The third firefly, called C, is at a lesser distance from A than B so the signal travelling at the speed of light gets back to A more quickly (the dotted line). So immediately, A can now say that it knows something. It knows that firefly C is closer than B. Distance is emergent. Also, the time skipped over (the amnesia) of firefly A is now less because it has interacted with C during that time so there is some time that it can measure smaller than the period T. Time is emergent too.

The general idea is that time (ageing) speeds up for more complex systems (like A, B and C) and slows down for simpler ones (A and B).

This also means that distances are not absolute. As is well known, we can only measure distance relative to the sizes of other things, such as for example the distance between Henry the First's nose and his fingertip (the yard). So A can never know exactly how far B and C are from it, but they are relational in that A can say that C is closer than B. The information is not exact, though. A cannot tell exactly how much closer C is than B because as far as it is concerned the time interval 1 to 2 (on the diagram) is equal to the time interval 2 to 3. It cannot resolve anything less than that.

As we walk around as complex entities surrounded by interactions with air, ground and the occasional passing maniac, there is far more interaction, so we have a fine sense of time compared to the systems I am discussing, but here the picture has been simplified to see the basics more clearly and I believe that these basics are still observable for simpler quantum systems.

It can be thought of as an extension of the philosophy of special relativity, in that Einstein proposed that the speed of light can be measured in different reference frames and had been found experimentally to be constant (frame independent) whereas abstracts like space and time cannot be measured, so he decided to modify space and time to keep the speed of light at its measured value in any frame to agree with the data.

Immediately one can see how this new approach might help with the strange behaviour of Young's two-slit experiment, the EPR paradox or Bell's inequality.[82] Since the particles in these quantum systems do not interact with anything between the time they are entangled and emitted, and the time they hit the screen or are detected, then time is not measurable for them and therefore, as suggested above, time does not pass for them and therefore as far as they are concerned when they are emitted the detector is already measuring them. Mathematically the time deleted T' is equal to the time elapsed, T. From our point of view then, it looks as if they can see a future that we cannot.

---

82   McCulloch, M.E. and J. Gine, 2021. The EPR paradox and the uncertainty principle. *MPL-B*, 35, 4, 2150072.

6.2 TO THE UNCERTAINTY PRINCIPLE

So far we have discussed two fireflys exchanging signals using light and thereby determining their separation. That is the only information available in this particular model universe, so to avoid being bored they are taking full advantage of it. One thing, though, that we must insist upon is that the wavelength of the light they use must not be longer than their separation.

The reason for this is that the only things in this universe are the two fireflys and so the only distance measurement that exists is the distance from A to B, so the wavelength must have this length, specifically the length from A to B and back again. No other distances can exist, since no other distances can be measured, but higher harmonics can exist too so wavelength (λ) can be less than this (but quantised). We can write this as

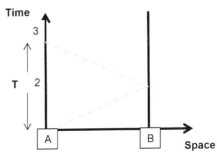

Figure 57. A and B can only measure the distance between them.

$$\lambda < 2x$$

Where λ is the wavelength and x is the separation of A from B. Since $c=f\lambda$ and $E=hf$ then $\lambda=hc/E$ so

$$\frac{hc}{E} < 2x$$

Rearranging and using $E=pc$ where p is momentum.

$$\frac{h}{2} < px$$

This is very similar to Heisenberg's uncertainty principle

$$\frac{\hbar}{2} < \Delta p \Delta x$$

This principle means that if one considers a particle which is confined to a smaller and smaller region then your information about its position increases. Therefore. the position uncertainty (Δx) you have about it must decrease and the momentum uncertainty of the particles within it (Δp) increases. This 'minimum allowed noise' is the origin of the zero point field: a sea of virtual particles that was first proposed by Albert Einstein and Otto Stern in 1913 to account for the observed specific heat of hydrogen at low temperatures.[83]

One succinct way to put the uncertainty principle is that one cannot have perfect knowledge of anything. Knowing we have

Figure 58. The Uncertainty Principle is no joke.

---

83   Einstein, A. and O. Stern, 1913. *Annalen der Physik*, 40, 551-60.

a 100% vacuum would be perfect knowledge, so therefore you can't have one.

6.3 RINDLER HORIZONS

Now let us bring motion in. In the schematic below, a firefly, denoted by B accelerates leftward. At first (see the top line) its speed is much less than c, so the black arrow shown here is short (Time = 1). Two photons follow it, called P1 and P2 (grey dots and arrows) and they carry information about the part of the cosmos they come from. At a later time (Time = 2), shown by the middle part of the schematic, photon P1 catches up to B, so B can know about it and know about the part of the cosmos P1 came from, but photon P2 has not caught up yet. At an even later time (Time = 3) B is travelling at light speed so poor P2, limited to light speed, will never catch up and B will never know anything about the zone where P2 came from.

There is obviously some distance between P1 and P2 at which photons can 'just' catch up (the black dashed line) and this is called the Rindler horizon. B will never receive information from behind that horizon, if it continues to accelerate.

How far away will this Rindler horizon be from object B? To calculate this we can simply use the Galilean equation of motion

$$v = u + at$$

where v is the final velocity you get when you start at a velocity u, and undergo an acceleration a for a time t. So the time B takes to reach light speed, c, at acceleration a, is

$$t = \frac{c - u}{a}$$

How far has light travelled in this time? Distance is speed times time, so

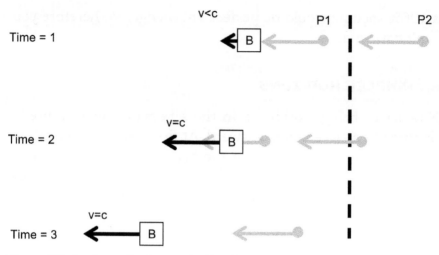

Figure 59. A schematic demonstrating the Rindler horizon.

$$d = c\left(\frac{c-u}{a}\right) = \frac{c^2}{a} - \frac{cu}{a}$$

We can assume that the initial velocity u was much smaller than the speed of light c (most velocities are!) so the second term is too small to worry about. A big number times a big number is a lot bigger than a big number times a small number, whatever those numbers are, so what is left is

$$d = \frac{c^2}{a}$$

This means that, according to special relativity, any information more than this distance behind an accelerated particle can never hope to reach it and so there is a shadow zone beyond that distance, and a so-called Rindler horizon divides the space that can be known from the space that can't.

Now, we can begin to introduce quantised inertia. We need to invoke a bit of logic here. If we say that a horizon is a boundary for information, we must go all the way. Not only must a horizon not allow information to pass through it, it also must not allow any sentient object to be able to determine what lies behind it and here we can also change from viewing the fireflys as inanimate matter, but start to view them as being 'observers' (not necessarily just humans, but also simple mechanisms) who can use clues from the environment to infer things and act on them.

6.4 UNRUH WAVES

As we just saw, when an object accelerates it sees a Rindler horizon (see the vertical black line below) which forces a node (a zero point for the wave) on the quantum vacuum just as a mirror would. In the case of a mirror, electrons moving in the metal cancel the electromagnetic field. In the case of a horizon it is more philosophical, in that a horizon must be a boundary to all information and if we allow a partial wave peak to straddle the horizon then we would be able to know the condition beyond the horizon. Therefore it is proposed that nature must impose nodes at horizons. Therefore the horizon tunes the quantum background so that only wavelengths with a node at the horizon and the accelerated object, as shown below by the dark grey curve, are allowed. Higher harmonics with similar nodes are also allowed, such as the light grey curve.

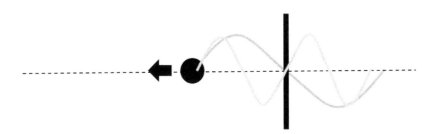

Figure 60. Selection of nodes by a Rindler horizon.

Now we can define the uncertainty in position to be the distance to the horizon, c^2/a. The longest allowed wave is twice the distance to the horizon, see the darker wave above, so we can just write

$$\lambda = \frac{2c^2}{a}$$

Or, going back to the uncertainty principle we derived above, we have

$$\Delta p \Delta x \sim \frac{h}{2}$$

and using $p=E/c$ and $E=hc/\lambda$ we get the same expression for wavelength.

This is the wavelength of the quantum radiation associated with these horizons. It is now called Fulling-Davies-Unruh radiation (or just Unruh radiation, for short)[84] and is similar to the Hawking radiation[85] emitted by black hole event horizons. In a similar way, we can say that event- or Rindler-horizons split virtual particle pairs so the one in front of the horizon can escape and become real. The 'Pinocchio Effect'?

So, what exactly is Unruh radiation? It is certainly a strange concept because if two objects, one with high and one with low acceleration look at the same space, they will see a different amount of Unruh radiation. It is thermal, so it is like the radiation emitted by a hot body, in which the electromagnetic waves are of various wavelengths, around a Planckian distribution and in random orientations. Not only that, since their definition comes from the quantum uncertainty principle, Unruh waves must be waves in all the fields: electromagnetic

84   Unruh, W.G., 1976. Notes on black hole evaporation. *Phys. Rev. D.*, 14, 870.

85   Hawking, S.W., 1976. Particle creation by black holes. *Comm. Math. Phys.* 43, 199-220.

and particle fields. In this book we will mainly consider their electromagnetic component.

6.5 QUANTISED GRAVITY

To show the power of this new approach let us model the gravity of two Planck masses side by side. Above, we showed that the fact that a wave must fit into a horizon, means that

$$a = \frac{c^2}{d}$$

Now $F = ma$, so we have

$$F = \frac{mc^2}{d} = \frac{E}{d} = \frac{hf}{d} = \frac{hc}{d\lambda}$$

Now we imagine the two fireflys, Planck masses, are in orbit around each other, one metre apart (distance d).

Figure 61. Two Planck masses in mutual orbit.

If we assume that one wave fits half way around an orbit, between the two Planck masses, then the wavelength λ = $\pi d/2$ and

$$F = \frac{2hc}{d \times \pi d} = \frac{2hc}{\pi d^2}$$

Now let us calculate the force we get for a separation of one metre

$$F = \frac{2 \times 6.626 \times 10^{-34} \times 3 \times 10^8}{\pi \times 1^2} = 12.65 \times 10^{-26}$$

Now what would Newtonian gravity predict? Remember that r=d/2

$$F = \frac{6.6743 \times 10^{-11} \times (2.176 \times 10^{-8})^2}{(1/2)^2} = 12.64 \times 10^{-26}$$

What a pleasant surprise! The force predicted is equal to the force that would be predicted by Newton's gravity law for two Planck masses, see also [86]: the holy grail of quantum gravity. This calculation is for Planck masses, on the border between the classical and quantum worlds. To apply it to larger masses, you just add the Planck masses together.

Interestingly, this implies that gravity requires an orbit, or at least that without an orbit, it is different.

How can we be sure that gravity is due to Unruh waves? It is well known from the equivalence principle, and observations, that the effects of gravity can be cancelled by acceleration. So, gravity is cancelled by acceleration (Unruh waves). Therefore it makes sense that gravity is made of Unruh waves—an emergent process caused by the Unruh waves being sheltered between physical bodies, akin to the Casimir effect between plates.

---

86   McCulloch, M.E., 2014. Gravity from the uncertainty principle. *Astrophys. Sp. Sci.*, 349, 957-959.

Figure 62. Gravity as an interplanetary Casimir effect. Love, not so much!
Note: MiHsC (Modified inertia by a Hubble-scale Casimir effect) is another name for QI.

6.6 QUANTISED INERTIA / MIHSC

Imagine a Planck mass, which is about the weight of a flea's egg, 2.17×10^{-8} kg and one Planck length l_p in size. It is accelerating to the right (dark double arrow) as shown in the schematic by the bifurcated black square (a square because at the Planck scale, shape makes no sense, so let's keep it simple). The particle sees a Rindler horizon to its left shown by one ver-

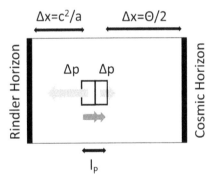

Figure 63. An accelerating Planck mass (the square) and associated horizons.

tical black line. It also sees a far-off cosmic horizon on its right (Another black line. Its distance is not to scale!).

Now let's return to the uncertainty relation for momentum (p) & position (x)

$$\Delta x \Delta p > \hbar/_2$$

In quantised inertia the new assumption is that the uncertainty in position Δx[87] is the distance to a horizon. So if Δx is small then Δp (which I interpret as jitter) is large. In the schematic above we can see that the Planck mass has a horizon close by on its left and one far-off to its right. This implies it will have more uncertainty in momentum (jitter) to the left (see the comparative size of the light grey arrows) and so it will tend to drift leftwards, against its initial acceleration (dark arrows). This predicts what we know as inertia, with a tiny difference that happens to predict galaxy rotation and many other anomalies without needing dark matter or dark energy.[88]

Let's derive this properly. On the right hand side of the Planck mass, the uncertainty in momentum is small (the grey arrow is short) because Δx, the cosmic horizon, is far away

$$\Delta p_R > \frac{\hbar}{(\Theta/_2)}$$

where Θ is the cosmic diameter which is not to be sneezed at, at 8.8×10^{26} metres. To the left of the Planck mass, the uncertainty in momentum is larger because the uncertainty in position is small. The distance to the Rindler horizon as c^2/a gives us

$$\Delta p_L > \frac{\hbar}{(c^2/_a)}$$

We now assume that Heisenberg's abstract concept of momentum uncertainty is real momentum (it works at a

---

87   A two-way uncertainty. We need half of it.

88   McCulloch, M.E., 2016. Quantised inertia from relativity and the uncertainty principle. *EPL*, 115, 69001.

quantum level, so at the level of a Planck mass it is still true). So we have a difference in the momentum from left to right so the total momentum in the x direction is $p = \Delta p_{Right} - \Delta p_{Left}$. The force on the mass is the differential of momentum with time

$$F = \frac{dp}{dt} = \frac{dp}{dx}\frac{dx}{dt}$$

Now let's replace the derivatives on the right with real numbers. The dp/dx is the difference between the momentum on left and right divided by the distance between them. Using the equations above $\Delta p_{Right} - \Delta p_{Left} = \hbar/(\Theta/2) - \hbar/(c^2/a)$. The distance between the two halves' centres is half the Planck length, $l_p/2$, so dp/dx= $(\hbar/(\Theta/2) - \hbar/(c^2/a))/(l_p/2)$. The dx/dt is the speed of information transfer: the speed of light, c. After some algebra we get

$$F = \frac{\hbar}{cl_p}\left(1 - \frac{2c^2}{a\Theta}\right)a = ma$$

Since Newton, we have assumed F=ma (Newton's second law). No longer. We now have the slightly different equation above which is the new paradigm of quantised inertia, first derived a different way in[89]. The difference is ridiculously small for the accelerations we encounter on Earth, or in the Solar system (unless we shrink the cosmic scale Θ using metal cavities, the walls of which are like horizons) but for tiny accelerations, such as at the edge of galaxies, the effect is real and well observed as the galaxy rotation problem. So here we have derived the standard formula for quantised inertia, where the part representing the mass is (ie: everything except 'a') is

---

89   McCulloch, M.E., 2007. *MNRAS*, 376, 338-342.

$$m = \frac{\hbar}{cl_p}\left(1 - \frac{2c^2}{a\Theta}\right)$$

Now you may be unnerved to see that this equation does not have the units of mass, but it all works out because $\hbar$ has the units of Js, and J=kgm²s⁻². The second term in the brackets is tiny for most accelerations we have experienced on Earth so we have, typically, the simplification where N is the number of Planck masses

$$F = \frac{N\hbar a}{cl_p} = ma$$

The value of $\hbar/cl_p$ is $2.18\times10^{-8}kg$: the Planck mass. We have derived a new expression for inertial mass, which also predicts galaxy rotations without dark matter. To calculate the mass of larger objects, you add up the Planck masses. Also, in QI, inertial mass is not a quantity intrinsic to objects as was believed until now, but it is due to their interactions with the cosmos.

QI predicts both inertia and gravity as emerging from gradients in the quantum vacuum (specifically Unruh radiation). Does this new physics allow us to predict the anomalies we went through in Chapter 5? Well, yes, a large number of them. Read on!

CHAPTER 7

EXPLAINING ANOMALIES

IN THIS CHAPTER I will demonstrate how quantised inertia predicts many of the anomalies discussed in Chapter 5. I can't claim yet that QI predicts all of them, or even the ones I mention below perfectly, because for broadness and to show you the range of subjects that can be tackled (in the hope that some of you will), I have included some results that are suggestive.

On the other hand, for some of them, such as the galactic cut-off, wide binaries or lab tests, only quantised inertia can possibly work. These are what Newton called 'Crucial Experiments' since they show that only the suggested hypothesis can be true and not any of its rivals.

7.1 COSMIC ACCELERATION

The Hubble expansion of the universe is accelerating. To explain this, unbelievable amounts of so-called dark energy have been invented out of nothing. Instead, using Newton's second and gravity law, and QI, we get

$$F = m\left(1 - \frac{2c^2}{a\Theta}\right)a = \frac{GMm}{r^2}$$

$$\therefore a = \frac{GM}{r^2} + \frac{2c^2}{\Theta}$$

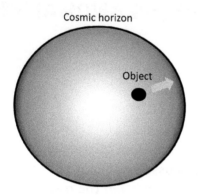

Cosmic horizon

Object

Figure 64. The Cosmos. A horizon causes an acceleration towards itself of *a = c²/d*. All matter will be pulled outwards towards the cosmic horizon, balancing the gravity inwards (a steady state).[89]

This predicts that the acceleration of any object has the standard first term, plus another new term of $2\times10^{-10}m/s^2$. This number crops up everywhere in astronomy as we have seen. If we consider the stars close to the cosmic edge, this is the cosmic acceleration attributed to dark energy. It is predicted by QI as a minimum acceleration required from all matter so that the Unruh waves they see are not larger than the observable cosmos, which would be illogical. A horizon should not allow us to infer anything beyond it. Crucially, this means that in QI, Newton's First Law is very slightly wrong–there can be no constant speed.

In Fig. 64 the white area has intense Unruh radiation (many allowed wavelengths), but the dark area, damped by the horizon, has fewer. Objects are pushed away from the centre by the greater quantum pressure there, just as ships are pushed

90   McCulloch, M.E., 2014. A toy cosmology using a Hubble-scale Casimir effect. Galaxies, 2, 1, 81-88.

towards the coast in a stormy sea, & gravity (also from QI, see section 6.5) pulls them centre-wards.

7.2 COSMIC FLATNESS PROBLEM

The cosmic flatness problem is the observation that the cosmic potential and kinetic energy are equal, or that the cosmos is just closed—poised between having enough kinetic energy to expand forever, and having so little that it will collapse back gravitationally onto itself. This requires too fine a tuning early on in cosmic history to be reasonable since any early deviation would grow exponentially.[91] So why is the cosmos flat? The critical density of the cosmos, the density at which it is flat, is $\rho_c = 3H^2/8\pi G$ where H is the Hubble constant. This can be rearranged using $H=2c/\Theta$, $\Theta=2r$ and by converting density ρ to a cosmic mass ($M_U = \rho_c \times$ cosmic volume), so

$$\frac{GM_U}{r} = \frac{1}{2}c^2$$

The cosmos has a potential energy, shown on the left hand side (GM/r), equal to the kinetic energy, shown on the right hand side. This observation can be derived easily from quantised inertia which says that in any given volume the acceleration must be at least large enough to make Unruh waves shorter than the size of that volume, ie

$$\frac{GM_U}{r^2} \geq \frac{2c^2}{\Theta}$$

This produces the result, since $\Theta = 2r$ that

---

91   Dicke, R.H, 1970. *Gravitation & the Universe: Jayne Lectures for 1969.* American Philosophical Society.

$$\frac{GM_U}{r} \geq c^2$$

OK, it's missing a factor of 1/2 but it is pretty close. QI gives a reason why the cosmos is flat–it has to be–and it erases the need to have early fine tuning of the cosmos or the ad hoc process of inflation, which proposed that the early cosmos expanded very fast to explain why it is now flat. The cosmos is flat because gravity and quantised inertia are always in balance.

7.3 VALUE OF THE GRAVITATIONAL CONSTANT, G

We can use the simple equation derived in Section 7.2 to derive the constant of physics G from observable data. We start with

$$\frac{GM_U}{r} = c^2$$

Where M_U is the cosmic mass. Therefore,

$$G = \frac{c^2 \Theta}{2M_U}$$

If we set the cosmic mass to be $M_U = 10^{53\pm1} kg$ (a reasonable value obtained from counting stars and note that the exponent has an uncertainty of one so can vary by a factor of 100) then we get a value that is consistent with G

$$G = (4 \text{ to } 400) \times 10^{-11\pm1} m^3 kg^{-1} s^{-2}$$

It has been pointed out by Dirac, Sciama & Unzicker[92] that something like the above relation holds observationally, but they did not derive it from a theory, as done here.

---

92   Unzicker, A., 2015. Einstein's Lost Key.

QI therefore erases Newton's gravitational constant, G, from physics, a useful simplification, because G can be calculated and replaced by the observable parameters: c, Θ and Mu. Newton's gravity law now reads

$$F = \frac{c^2 \Theta}{2 M_U} \frac{Mm}{r^2}$$

This formula now has no arbitrary values. Everything on the right hand side can be measured. The other advantage of all this is that it would please Ernst Mach, who could have done with a little cheering up in his lifetime. As he suspected, gravity here is indeed due to an interaction with the rest of the cosmos.

7.4 GALAXY ROTATION PROBLEM

Stars at the edges of galaxies orbit too fast. To model this using quantised inertia[93] [94] we start with Newton's second and gravity laws, for a star of mass m orbiting a galaxy of mass M at radius r as follows

$$F = m_i a = \frac{GMm}{r^2}$$

Replacing inertial mass using QI, $m_i = m(1 - 2c^2/a\Theta)$ and splitting the acceleration $|a|$ into a slowly varying (rotational) part $a = v^2/r$ and a variable part a' due to inhomogeneities in the mass distribution, gives

$$\left(|a| + |a'| - \frac{2c^2}{\Theta} \right) a = \frac{GM(|a| + |a'|)}{r^2}$$

---

93   McCulloch, M.E., 2012. Testing quantised inertia on galactic scales. *Astrophys. Sp. Sci*, 342, 575-578.

94   McCulloch, M.E., 2017. Galaxy rotations from quantised inertia and visible matter only. ApSS, 362,149.

At the edge of a galaxy, $|a|$ becomes small, so the acceleration must stay above the minimum acceleration allowed in QI by the value of a', and so $a' = 2c^2/\Theta$. Therefore the second and third terms cancel. Now $a = v^2/r$ so

$$v^4 = GM(|a| + |a'|)$$

At the very edge of the galaxy the overall acceleration $|a|$ is small, but the local acceleration $a' = 2c^2/\Theta$ must remain large, so this simplifies to

$$v^4 = GMa' = \frac{2GMc^2}{\Theta}$$

This agrees with the observed Tully-Fisher relation (section 5.7) which predicts the orbital speed of galactic edge stars. QI also predicts something that no other theory can. MoND predicts $v^4 = GMa_0$ where a_0 is constant, but the cosmic scale in the QI equation above (Θ) predicts that in the past when the observable cosmos (not the physical cosmos) was smaller, the galactic edge velocity was larger. So QI predicts that early galaxies should spin faster at the same mass. This has been shown to be the case[95].

7.5 COSMIC CLOCKS

All the galaxies observed so far rotate at their edges in around one billion years, and standard physics has no explanation for these cosmic clocks[96]. There is a possible explanation from QI and its implications for time[97]. Starting from the uncertainty principle

95   Genzel R., et al., 2017. *Nature*, 543, 397-401.

96   Meurer et al., 2018. Cosmic clocks: A Tight Radius–Velocity Relationship for HI-Selected Galaxies. *MNRAS*, 476, 1624-1636.

97   McCulloch, M.E. and J. Gine, 2021. The EPR paradox and the uncertainty principle. *MPL-B*, 35, 4, 2150072.

$$\Delta E \Delta t \geq \hbar/2$$

The uncertainty in energy (ΔE) times the uncertainty in time (Δt) must be greater than or equal to the right hand side. If we assume we have thermal energy then E=kT and we can use the Unruh temperature T=ħa/2πck so

$$\Delta t \geq \frac{\pi c}{a}$$

This implies that the uncertainty is time is higher for low accelerations so, as discussed at the beginning of Chapter 6, time will slow down. The acceleration (a) at the edges of galaxies has a minimum of about 2×10^{-10} m/s² (itself explained by QI). Putting this in the equation above gives 149 billion years. This is 149 times too large but it could explain why the edges of galaxies rotate in unison–they all tend towards the same minimum acceleration and so they have the same minimum time interval (slow time).

One way to think about it is that systems that have an acceleration that is very slow, see Unruh waves that are very long, in QI the only way they can measure time is relative to the peaks of those passing waves. Since the waves take so long to pass, their 'time' must be slowed down. The period of a wave T = wavelength/speed. For time to be measured, a quarter of a wave is enough so the period = $\Theta/4c = 7\times10^{17}$s. This is 23 billion years.

7.6 FROM QI TO SIMPLE MOND

As before, we start from Newton's second & gravity law, with the usual tweak to inertial mass from QI:

$$F = \frac{GMm}{r^2} = m_i a = m\left(1 - \frac{2c^2}{a\Theta}\right)a$$

In the MoND theory (MoND stands for Modified Newtonian Dynamics[98]), what we have in QI as $2c^2/\Theta$ requires instead an empirical fitted constant called a_0. Replacing this in the formula above we get

$$F = m\left(1 - \frac{a_0}{a}\right) a \sim m\left(\frac{1}{1 + a_0/a}\right)$$

This is the so-called 'simple' MoND formula, where a_0 is Milgrom's constant, but in QI we know that a_0 can be broken down into $2c^2/\Theta$, and this gives QI much greater predictive power both over cosmic time & for small cavities.

First, QI predicts that a_0 varies over time as Θ varies (see section 7.4), so physics looked different in the past, as seems to be the case.

Secondly, the QI effect will also vary when we have smaller horizons than the cosmic one—such as in metal cavities in the lab for which Θ is also much smaller because the metal enforces a node in Unruh waves just as abstract horizons do. This usefully brings cosmology into the lab, and makes it directly testable—Applied Cosmology!—see later in this book.

7.7 CHANGE IN HUBBLE'S CONSTANT WITH TIME

As stated above, unlike MoND, which uses a constant critical acceleration a_0 which is 'set' by comparison to the data, quantised inertia predicts this value itself without the need for tuning. It is $2c^2/\Theta$. This depends on the speed of light, c, and the co-moving diameter of the cosmos, Θ, which increases with time (or decreases into the past) and so QI predicts a change in galaxy rotation with

---

98   Milgrom, M., 1983. A modification of the Newtonian dynamics as a possible alternative to the hidden mass hypothesis. *Astrophysical Journal*, Vol. 270, p. 365-370.

time. The cosmic diameter Θ, assuming a linear expansion of the cosmos with time, depends on the redshift (Z) as

$$\Theta_{atz} = \frac{\Theta_{now}}{1 + Z}$$

Therefore, quantised inertia predicts that the acceleration on the edge of galaxies should show a dependence on distance or redshift, Z. At higher Z (further back in cosmic time) the galaxy rotation problem should be more obvious (everything else, such as galaxy evolution, being considered) so that equal-mass galaxies observed in the distant past should spin faster. Let's consider the mass required to produce a particular rotation speed. Using the formula derived in section 7.4 and the one above, we get

$$v^4 = \frac{2GMc^2(1 + Z)}{\Theta_{now}}$$

So that the amount of mass associated with a rotation speed of v is

$$M = \frac{v^4 \Theta_{now}}{2Gc^2(1 + Z)}$$

There is now evidence for this both in terms of mass and speed.[99] [100] The Genzel et al. paper referenced below is especially amusing because it was published in Nature a few months after my paper predicting this effect had been rejected by Nature.

99   Ubler et al., 2017. *Astrophysical Journal*, 842, 2, 121.

100   Genzel et al., 2020. *Nature*, 543, 397-401.

7.8 LOW-L CMB ANOMALY

The low-l Cosmic Microwave Background (CMB) anomaly is the observation that the cosmos is unexpectedly smooth on the largest scales. In quantised inertia, long waves are disallowed so the energy of the CMB blackbody radiation spectrum E should be modified to E' as follows

$$E' = E\left(1 - \frac{\lambda_m}{4\Theta}\right)$$

where λ_m is the wavelength of the part of the CMB we are looking at and Θ is the Hubble diameter. In other words, when λ_m is nearly as long as Θ there should be a reduction in CMB energy. The CMB data is presented with respect to the monopole moment, and the first monopole moment (l=1, or with a less ambiguous letter: L=1) indicates the longest wave observable in the sky, which has a wavelength equal to the width of the sky: 2Θ. Therefore, the monopole moment can be written in terms of the Hubble diameter, and assuming a flat space, as $L = 2\Theta/\lambda_m$ so

$$E' = E\left(1 - \frac{1}{2L}\right)$$

Therefore, for higher multipoles, or smaller cosmic scales, the effect of quantised inertia (a Hubble-scale Casimir effect) is negligible, since L is large and the second term in the brackets is small. However, for low multipoles, or very long wavelengths, where the observed low-l CMB anomaly occurs, the value of L is smaller, the second term in the brackets becomes more important, and the reduction in energy is more significant.

As observed by the Planck Collaboration in 2013 there was a significant 5 to 10% reduction in power below that expected from the Λ-CDM for all the multipoles (L) less than 40. This agrees with the QI prediction[101].

In other words, many of the longest wavelengths are being deselected by the cosmic horizon. We could call this effect a Cosmic Seiche[102].

7.9 PEAKS OF THE CMB

The Cosmic Microwave Background is assumed to have formed when the cosmos, or rather the part of it we can see, was 200 times smaller. So instead of the scale being 360 degrees (right around the sky) the scale is 360/200 degrees or $\lambda_0=1.8°$. According to quantised inertia this is the maximum Unruh wavelength, or wavelength of any wave, allowed in this smaller cosmos.

Higher harmonics, half that wavelength, then wavelengths divided by three...etc, would also fit. So $\lambda_n = \lambda_0/2, \lambda_0/3, \lambda_0/4$.... This means we can try to predict the CMB peaks from quantised inertia. The result is shown here:

Observed CMB peak (°)	Predicted CMB peak (°)
1.8	1.8
0.72	0.9
0.45	0.6
0.31	0.45
0.25	0.36

---

101 McCulloch, M.E., 2014. A toy cosmology using a Hubble-scale Casimir effect. *Galaxies*, 2(1),81-88.

102 Seiches occur in harbours where long waves that have nodes at the harbour walls are enhanced and waves that do not exactly fit are damped. The enhanced waves may cause flooding. This effect can also cause problems in the bath if you slosh the water at a particular frequency!

The agreement is not perfect, but the basis number 1.8° is far from certain. The peaks in the CMB spectrum would be a nice illustration of the ideas behind quantised inertia. It is a visible sign that of all the waves in the cosmos, only those with harmonics that fit exactly into the cosmic horizon are allowed. Again, a Cosmic Seiche.

7.10 MASS IS AREA

In QI, it is impossible for the acceleration of an object to fall below a minimum value of $2c^2/\Theta$ because then the Unruh radiation it sees would have a wavelength longer than the cosmic scale and be unobservable. Another way to state this is that the information horizons they see would lie behind the cosmic horizon which is also impossible. So, in any spherical region of space of radius r, if we assume that only gravity is acting, then gravity must be large enough to keep all matter above this acceleration:

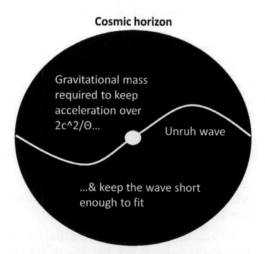

Figure 65. The longest Unruh wave that fits in the cosmos.

$$\frac{GM}{r^2} > \frac{2c^2}{\Theta}$$

where M is the gravitational mass that must exist to maintain the minimum acceleration of QI & keep Unruh waves visible. Therefore

$$M > \frac{2c^2 r^2}{G\Theta}$$

Taking the standard values for the speed of light, c, the gravitational constant, G, and the Hubble diameter $\Theta = 8.8 \times 10^{26} m$ then we get

$$M > \frac{2c^2 r^2}{G\Theta} > 3.067 r^2$$

This is within 2% of the formula below and the uncertainty in Θ is about 10% via the Hubble constant[103] so amazingly we can write

$$M > \pi r^2$$

Yes. I hear you ask. Units! It is quite peculiar, but it does make some sense since the units of $2c^2/G\Theta$ are kg/m^2 or mass per unit area. This is analogous to general relativity to some extent since mass in that theory is defined as the curvature of space (though I do not like the abstract, untestable, principle of bent space, this link may mean something deeper). The more mass in a given space, the more bent that space is, and so the lower the value of Pi. The prediction is that M/r^2 should be close to Pi.

Also, from the second equation back, by cancelling the r^2 on both sides, you can get $2c^2/\Theta=G\pi$ (this was pointed out by my editor, R. Zubrin).

---

103 Freedman, 2001.

The relation between mass and area has also been mentioned by Unzicke[104] who pointed out that the total surface area of the galaxies in the observable universe is approximately equivalent to the spherical surface area of the Hubble sphere, and pointed out that this is "a remarkable property of the present era". Further he pointed out that for both the Solar system and the cosmos, a spherical shell of protons covering these volumes has the same mass as the matter inside these areas.

The new advance here is that there is no reason for it to be a 'special property of the present era' with quantised inertia, since from the equation above the mass increases as the cosmic horizon does, so it is a property of every era. QI is a simplification of physics by erasing the arbitrary.

7.11 THE VARIABLE SPEED OF LIGHT

We can play around with the equation derived in Section 7.2 comparing the kinetic energy and the potential energy of the cosmos. This is

$$\frac{GM}{r} = c^2$$

Therefore,

$$c = \sqrt{\frac{2GM}{\Theta}}$$

Since, as we saw in 7.10, that mass is the flat area of the cosmos, and $\Theta = 2r$, then

$$c = \sqrt{G\pi r}$$

---

104 Unzicker, A., 2015. Einstein's Lost Key. A well-written and crucial resurrection of a brilliant idea.

This only works out if 'π' is in units of kgm⁻². Putting in values we see that c = 303,644,000 m/s. This is within 1% of the speed of light and predicts that the speed of light increases with time as r increases. Differentiating

$$\frac{dc}{dt} = \sqrt{\frac{G\pi}{r}\frac{c}{2}} = 10^{-10}ms^{-2}$$

This predicted acceleration of light is half of the cosmic acceleration, predicted in other ways by QI as $2c^2/\Theta = 2\times10^{-10}$ m/s². This could be because it is accelerating both to the left and right.

7.12 ARP'S QUANTISED REDSHIFT

Halton Arp[105] noticed that quasars are quantised at particular redshifts, such as Z=0.3, 0.6, 0.96, 1.96, 2.6 and 3.5 (as ever, this is relatively new and therefore hotly debated). Now let us consider the inertial mass of electrons in atoms according to quantised inertia. In an atom, the electrons accelerate circularly and have a quantised inertial mass (m')

$$\frac{m'}{m} = \left(1 - \frac{2c^2}{a\Theta}\right)$$

We can express this ratio of masses, using $E = mc^2$, as a ratio of energies and then, using $E = hc/\lambda$, as a ratio of wavelengths

$$\frac{\lambda}{\lambda'} = 1 - \frac{2c^2}{a\Theta}$$

Arp, H., 1998. Seeing Red. A bold, and also poignant book, as he describes the obstacles he faced.

The redshifts we see from quasars originated from light emitted from electron transitions. Using the definition of redshift (Z) and QI we get

$$Z = \frac{\Delta\lambda}{\lambda} = \frac{\lambda' - \lambda}{\lambda} = \frac{\lambda'}{\lambda} - 1 = \frac{1}{1 - 2c^2/a\Theta} - 1$$

In order for the Unruh waves seen by the electrons to fit within their orbit, in the same way that quantum waves do, the allowed accelerations are $a = (8c^2/\pi\Theta)\times n$, where n is 1, 2, 3..etc. Substituting this into the equation gives

$$Z = \frac{1}{4n/\pi - 1}$$

This formula predicts Z=3.65, 0.65 and 0.35 as observed but also other quantised redshifts such as 0.24 and 0.18 that are not seen. The other redshifts seen by Arp but not predicted here could be due to other atomic transitions not considered here. Feel free to try it: be the next J.J. Balmer!

7.13 A TASTE OF QI COSMOLOGY

As we have discussed above, QI says that matter must be created so that the acceleration in each volume sphere must stay above $2c^2/\Theta$ so that the Unruh waves are shorter than the diameter of the volume. What cannot be seen must not exist, so

$$\frac{GM}{r^2} > \frac{2c^2}{\Theta}$$

This leads to

$$\frac{GM}{r} > c^2$$

This immediately tells us that the potential energy (left hand side) of the cosmos must be equal to or greater than the kinetic energy. Putting the known numbers for the cosmos in here, we find that this formula is actually an equality.

The second point is that, if we go back into the past, the observed size of the cosmos (r) decreases, so the speed of light could have been greater. Furthermore, since c=fλ and f must stay constant for travelling light (constant energy, hf) then λ must have been greater in the past and so distant light is red-shifted. This implies redshift is not due to a physical expansion of the cosmos and the Doppler effect due to that, but rather the fact that distant light was formed when the cosmos was smaller and the QI physics was different. Rearranging the equation above we get

$$c = \sqrt{\frac{GM}{r}}$$

This is an equation for the orbit of a photon around the cosmos' rim, with a balance between gravity pulling it in, and inertia pushing it out, in contrast to section 7.11 which was an equation for the outwards acceleration of c.

7.14 MAGELLANIC CLOUDS

The Large and Small Magellanic clouds (LMC and SMC, see 5.16) are satellite galaxies just outside the Milky Way who orbit far too fast to be bound, but they must be bound because the trail they leave (see the schematic) is curved around the Milky Way.

Figure 66. The small and large Magellanic clouds.

If we assume Newtonian physics and that the Milky Way has only baryonic (normal) matter, we get an orbital speed of

$$v = \sqrt{\frac{GM}{r}} = 136 km/s$$

where M is the Milky Way's mass ($2 \times 10^{11} M_{sol}$, ie: 2×10^{11} times the mass of the Sun) and r is the radial distance of the LMC (48 kpc). The maximum orbital speed allowed by Newton is 136 km/s but the observed orbital speed is 378 km/s so the LMC should be flying away from our galaxy. It's not!

Quantised inertia says that because of their low acceleration outside the galaxy, the SMC & LMC have lost some inertial mass and so the centrifugal force forcing them away is less than we expect. QI predicts the following orbital speed, the second term being due to quantised inertia:

$$v = \sqrt{\frac{GM}{r} + \frac{2c^2r}{\Theta}} = 560 \ km/s$$

where c is the speed of light and Θ is the Hubble diameter. The observed orbital velocity of the LMC is 378 km/s, so QI predicts that the LMC is bound to the Milky Way and this is consistent with the observation of the Magellanic Stream that shows a bound past trajectory for it.

7.15 WIDE BINARIES

Wide binaries (see 5.17) are stars so far apart (>7000 AUs) that their mutual acceleration is as low as stars at the edge of galaxies. Sure enough, they show the same odd dynamics that the galactic edge stars do[106]. This means that dark matter cannot be the cause of either, since it must stay spread out to work in galaxies. Can true theorists do intellectual splits? No.

Here, we recapitulate this paper[107]. Starting with Newton's second law and gravity law, replacing the inertial mass using QI and naming M_g as M gives

$$F = M\left(1 - \frac{2c^2}{|a|\Theta}\right)\frac{2v^2}{d} = \frac{GMM}{d^2}$$

where $|a|$ is the modulus of the total acceleration of the orbiting stars relative to the fixed stars, which is $a=2v^2/d$ (the radial centrifugal component) plus the non-centrifugal acceleration of $2c^2/\Theta$. Therefore

$$\frac{GM}{2d} = v^2 - \frac{2c^2v^2}{\left(\frac{2v^2}{d} + \frac{2c^2}{\Theta}\right)\Theta}$$

Rearranging and using the quadratic formula, we get the following

$$\Delta v_{QI} = \sqrt{\frac{GM}{d} + \sqrt{\frac{G^2M^2}{d^2} + \sqrt{\frac{8GMc^2}{\Theta}}}}$$

106 Hernandez, X., S. Cookson, RAM, Cortes, 2022. *MNRAS*, 509, 2, 2304-2317.

107 McCulloch, M.E. and J. Lucio, 2019. *Astro. Space Sci.*, 364, 121.

This formula has the advantage over MoND in that it has $2c^2/\Theta$ instead of a_0 (the adjustable MoND parameter), so all the parameters are fixed and known, so it cannot be tuned. It either works or it does not. It does! It predicts the orbital speed of wide binaries perfectly. Newton or general relativity do not (as said above, dark matter cannot be used on these small scales as it must stay spread out on galactic scales). MoND also fails due to its external field effect. This is probably the most conclusive proof of QI.

7.16 HOAG'S OBJECT

This is a galaxy discovered by Hoag in 1950[108] (see 5.19) that has a bright yellow central core and a spectacular ring of blue stars surrounding it. Very pretty. There are a number of similar systems (they comprise 0.1% of all galaxies) but this is the poster child because it is directly facing us.

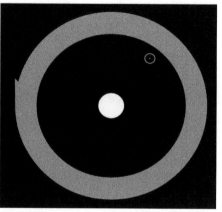

Figure 67. Hoag's Object.

Its mass is equivalent to 300 billion Suns and the radius of the ring is 35,000 light years, so we can calculate the radial gravitational acceleration at the outer ring.

$$a = \frac{GM}{r^2} = 3.62 \times 10^{-10} m/s^2$$

108 Hoag, A.A. 1950. A peculiar object in Serpens. *Astronomical Journal*. 55, 170.

Aha! By now this number should look familiar to you. This is close to the acceleration at the edge of all disc galaxies, wide binaries, Proxima Centauri...etc, a minimum acceleration that is predicted by quantised inertia as $2c^2/\Theta = 2 \times 10^{-10} m/s^2$.

The intuitive QI explanation is that matter has been ejected from the core, but is unable to get beyond the radius of the outer ring because, although its gravitational attraction to the centre reduces as $1/r^2$ as usual, its inertial mass reduces far more rapidly due to QI, until, at this radius its inertia becomes close to zero and it is attracted easily back towards the core even by the small forces out there.

This is possibly the most photogenic illustration of QI.

7.17 PROXIMA CENTAURI

The Alpha Centauri system has two close stars A and B at a distance apart of 10-30 AU[109] and a combined mass of 2±0.11 Solar masses[110] and one star much further away: Proxima, at a distance of 15,000±700 AU, with a mass of 0.123±0.006 Solar masses[111]. All three are co-moving and have similar chemistry, which implies they are bound, but the fast orbit of Proxima (0.53±0.14 km/s) implies it should fly off into space given the visible mass of A and B. Newton's laws predict that the maximum speed Proxima can have to stay bound to A & B is $v=\sqrt{GM/r}$= 0.34 km/s.

This problem cannot be fixed by dark matter, which must be uniform on these scales. It cannot be solved by adding mass to A and B—their mass is well known from their mutual close orbit. MoND cannot explain this anomaly due to its External Field Effect—the absolute acceleration of Proxima is still high, as it is not at the galactic edge. QI, in contrast, only considers the

---

109   1AU = 1 Astronomical Unit = 1.5×10^{-11}m

110   Anasova et al., 1994. *Astronomy and Astrophysics*, 292, 115.

111   Segransan et al., 2003. *Astronomy and Astrophysics*, 397, 3, L5-8.

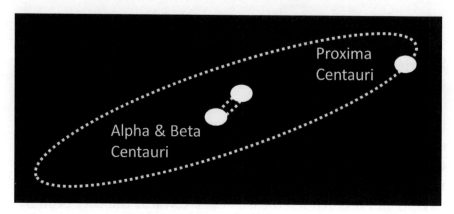

Figure 68. The Alpha Centauri System

mutual acceleration between bodies to work out their interaction. The velocity from QI is

$$v = \left(\frac{2GMc^2}{\Theta}\right)^{1/4} = 0.48 \pm 0.01 km/s$$

Therefore, in quantised inertia, Proxima Centauri's observed orbital velocity of 0.53±0.14*km/s* is consistent with the QI prediction, and so it is now consistent with the chemical and co-moving data that suggests that Proxima is bound. The old physics is not even valid for our closest neighbour in space– who is kindly helping to correct it for us.

7.18 BENDING OF LIGHT BY THE SUN.

One of the four basic tests of general relativity was its correct prediction of the bending of star light by the Sun. Here it is shown that quantised inertia predicts this also. We start from Newton's familiar gravity law

$$F = \frac{GMm}{r^2}$$

where F is the gravitational force, G is the gravitational 'constant', M and m are the two masses and r is the distance between them. To apply this dynamically to a photon we need the acceleration, so we use Newton's second law F=m_ia, where m_i is the inertial mass

$$a = \frac{GMm}{m_i r^2}$$

We are using QI to modify m_i, so after a little algebra

$$a = \frac{GM}{r^2} + \frac{2c^2}{\Theta}$$

What direction does the second term on the right act in? It represents a lessening of the Rindler pullback of QI due to the cosmic horizon pulling the other way, so it must be in a direction opposite to this pullback, and so, in the same direction as the initial acceleration. To get the velocity of the photon as it passes by the Sun, we integrate from a distance r to infinity

$$\int_r^\infty a \, dr = \int_r^\infty \frac{GM}{r^2} + \frac{2c^2}{\Theta} \, dr$$

In earlier works on quantised inertia it was assumed that Θ was the constant distance to the cosmic horizon ($8.8 \times 10^{26} m$) but in QI the distance to the cosmic horizon depends on the speed of light. As in section 7.2 we have $2c^2/\Theta = GM/r^2$ so $\Theta = 2r^2 c^2/GM$. For the cosmos as a whole $\Theta = 2r$, where r is the radius so $c^2 = 2GM/\Theta$. This relation has been verified from the data and had been suspected for some time[112]. Therefore

---

112 Unzicker, A., 2015. Einstein's Lost Key.

$$\int_r^\infty a\,dr = \int_r^\infty \frac{GM}{r^2} + \frac{GM}{r^2}\,dr$$

Which is

$$c[v]_r^\infty = \left[-\frac{2GM}{r} \right]_r^\infty = -\frac{2GM}{r}$$

Dividing through by c^2

$$\frac{c_r}{c_\infty} = 1 - \frac{2GM}{rc_\infty^2}$$

This formula predicts the observed Solar light deflection and timing results that have been used as direct tests of general relativity and provides an alternative, much simpler, mechanism.

To explain it more intuitively, Newton predicted that photons are bent towards the sun (with half the observed effect) but quantised inertia also predicts that the closer horizon they see, damps the Unruh waves they see, reducing their inertial mass and so doubling the bending.

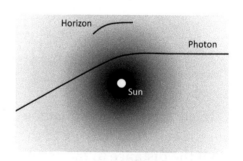

For the full derivation see[113] What this means is that QI can outperform general relativity in galaxies, and equal it in the Solar system.

Figure 69. A light beam bent by the Sun.

---

113 McCulloch, M.E., 2022. Testing QI on the bending of light by the Sun. Research Square.

QI predicts that horizons produce inhomogeneities in Unruh radiation (testable) which produce GR-like dynamics, instead of bent space. I never liked bent space, which is impossible to test directly. This QI model is directly testable and fits better with the 1911-1912 Variable Speed of Light version of GR proposed by Einstein and later corrected by Dicke, see[114]

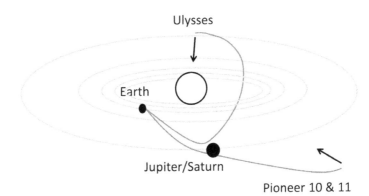

Ulysses

Earth

Jupiter/Saturn

Pioneer 10 & 11

Figure 70. Pioneer & Ulysses spacecraft trajectories.

7.19 PIONEER/ULYSSES ANOMALY

The Pioneer 10 and 11 spacecraft and the Ulysses spacecraft in orbit round the Sun showed anomalous accelerations of $8.74 \times 10^{-10} m/s^2$ (Pioneer) and $12 \times 10^{-10} m/s^2$ (Ulysses) towards the Sun (see the arrows on the schematic).

This was the anomaly that started me off toward QI[115] but it is now controversial as a complex thermal explanation has also been proposed. As above, in QI you simply combine Newton's second and gravity laws, and replace the inertial mass m_i with the quantised inertial mass to get

---

114 Unzicker, A., 2015. Einstein's Lost Key.

115 McCulloch, 2007. Modelling the Pioneer anomaly as modified inertia. *MNRAS*, 376, 338-342.

$$a = \frac{GM}{r^2} + \frac{2c^2}{\Theta}$$

This predicts an acceleration of $2 \times 10^{-10} m/s^2$ towards the Sun which is one quarter of the observed anomaly. At the time, I was using a much smaller value for the cosmic scale and so the prediction was 6.7×10^{-10} m/s^2.

With the thermal explanation[116] the residual anomaly is now about 2×10^{-10} m/s^2 so perhaps there is room for both explanations.

7.20 FLYBY ANOMALIES

The flyby anomalies are unexplained velocity jumps in spacecraft that approach at Earth's equator and leave closer to the poles. The pattern of these flybys is predicted by QI[117] but a few of the recent flybys have shown no anomaly where one might be expected. The way you derive the QI formula to predict the flybys is to consider the conservation of momentum for the Earth plus spacecraft. If the craft comes in at the equator, then its acceleration vector is pointing at us, but, as the Earth is spinning, all the Planck masses in the planet are accelerating (a) towards and away from the craft so the mutual acceleration, which is important for QI, is large. When the craft is leaving at the Pole, its acceleration vector is pointing down at the Pole but the Earth's Planck masses have acceleration vectors towards the rotation axis, perpendicular, so the mutual acceleration is lower. As a result, QI predicts the craft loses inertia over the Pole (spin axis), and to conserve momentum it has to speed up, hence the flyby anomalies.

---

116 Turyshev, S. et al., 2012. Support for the Thermal Origin of the Pioneer Anomaly. *Phys. Rev. Lett.* 108, 241101

117 McCulloch, M.E., 2008. Modelling the flyby anomalies... *MNRAS*, 389 (1), L57-60.

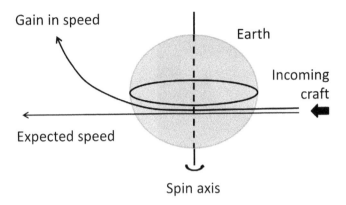

Figure 71. Flyby trajectories.

The change in speed (dv) depends on the crafts' initial and final speeds (v_1, v_2), accelerations (a_1, a_2) and latitudes (ϕ_1, ϕ_2) the Earth's radius (R) and equatorial rotation speed (v_e) and $a = (0.07v_e^2/R)cos\phi$. The result is

$$dv = \frac{2c^2}{\Theta}\left(\frac{v_2}{a_2} - \frac{v_1}{a_1}\right) = \frac{\beta\pi^2Rc^2}{0.07v_e^2\Theta}\left(\frac{v_2cos\varphi_1 - v_1cos\varphi_2}{cos\varphi_1cos\varphi_2}\right)$$

The agreement is good for the earlier flybys. For the later Juno flyby the observed anomaly was less than that predicted. It is possible that this also explains the apparent 'dark' mass along the spin axis of the Bullet cluster.

7.21 RELATIVISTIC JETS

Many galaxies emit fast jets of material along their spin axis. For example, M87 appears to emit material at six times the speed of light, 6c[118] According to Rees[119] this speed, given the

118 Biretta, 1999. Hubble space telescope observations of superluminal motion in the M87 jet. *The Astrophysical Journal*, 520, 2, 621-626.

119 Rees, 1966. Appearance of relativistically expanding radio sources. *Nature*, 211, 468-470.

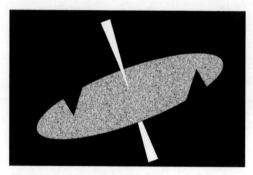

Figure 72. Relativistic jets.

likely angle of emission, is more likely close to 2-3c but it is still apparently superluminal, as it is for quite a few galaxies[120] Is this possible? What causes it?

Quantised inertia provides a much simpler explanation. Imagine a photon that, for some reason, crosses the spin axis of the galaxy. Exactly on the spin axis the mutual acceleration between it and the galaxy is tiny and so by QI it will lose its inertial mass and by conservation of momentum it will speed up. This is similar to the flyby anomalies that we discussed above, in which spacecraft sped up along the Earth's spin axis (the poles). We end up with a similar formula, but for photons, with c instead of speed v:

$$dv = \frac{2c^2}{\Theta}\left(\frac{c}{a_2} - \frac{c}{a_1}\right)$$

Now imagine the photon is already moving largely vertically (in the schematic) when it hits the axis. Initially its acceleration (a_1) was large, then it declines to $2c^2/\Theta$ (it cannot go any lower in QI) so we get

$$dv = \frac{2c^2}{\Theta}\left(\frac{c}{(2c^2/\Theta)} - \frac{c}{large}\right) = c$$

120 Porcas, 1987. Superluminal motion—astronomers still puzzled. *Nature*, 302, 753-754.

Therefore, if the photon was initially travelling upwards with speed c, now it will have speed 2c. I won't go into the massive difficulties with causality this implies, and I will just present it here with a Cheshire cat smile.

7.22 VARIATIONS IN THE GRAVITATIONAL CONSTANT

Variations in the gravitational "constant" have been found by many torsion balance experiments, G varying depending on the mutual acceleration of the gravitational masses used[121]. The Figure shows a typical experiment[122]. There are four small balls (each of mass 1.2 kg) on an inner ring of radius 120mm and four larger balls (each of mass 11 kg) on an outer ring of radius 214 mm, free to rotate. The outer four masses on the ring are placed at an angle to the inner masses which are pulled to the side, a pull that can be measured using the twist in a supporting wire, and G inferred.

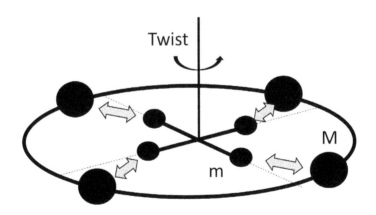

Figure 73. A typical experiment to measure G.

121 Klein, N., 2016. Are gravitational constant measurement discrepancies linked to galaxy rotation curves? https://arxiv.org/abs/1610.09181

122 Quinn, T., C. Speake & R. Davis, 2013. *Phys. Rev. Lett.*, 101102.

Now using Newton's 2nd and gravity laws and using the QI inertial mass, we can derive the acceleration a between the four masses, which is

$$a \sim \frac{GM}{r^2}\left(1 + \frac{c^2 r^2}{2G\Theta M}\right)$$

This means that the apparent change in G (ΔG, actually a change in inertia) should depend on the distance between the balls, r, and their mass, M. Putting in values, the predicted ΔG is about 1.1 parts per thousand. Quinn and Speake's observed value for ΔG/G was about 0.3 parts per thousand. According to QI, the result of [123] who used 13 tonnes of Mercury should have had a much lower ΔG, as M was so much bigger, and indeed it did. Now, when someone says G is constant, you have the balls to say "No."

7.23 HAYASAKA'S SPINNERS

Hayasaka[124] performed a free-fall experiment in which he enclosed spinning gyros in freefalling capsules. He found that for right spinning gyros (anticlockwise as seen from above) of diameter 5.8 cm and at 18,000 rpm (R), the fall-accelerations were smaller by 0.108 gal ($1.08 \times 10^{-3} ms^{-2}$). The gal was named after Galileo and 1gal = $1cms^{-1}$.

To calculate the effect of QI we use the conservation of momentum in the vertical and use the same equation as section 7.20 (the flyby anomalies)

$$dv = \frac{2c^2}{\Theta}\left(\frac{v_2}{a_2} - \frac{v_1}{a_1}\right)$$

123   Schlamminger, S., 2014. *Phil. Trans. Roy. Soc.*, 372, 20140027.

124   Hayasaka, H., H. Tanaka, T. Hashida, T. Chubachi and T. Sugiyama, 1997. *Speculations in Science and Technology*, 20, 173-181.

This dv is the change in velocity of the test mass to conserve momentum following changes in the acceleration of it relative to its surroundings $(a_1 \neq a_2)$ which changes the object's inertial mass by QI. The a_1 is the initial acceleration of the disc relative to the fixed stars $(a_s \sim 0.03\text{m/s}^2$, at mid-latitudes). The later acceleration caused by the spin we apply (a_2) is high, so we can ignore the first term in the brackets, and then we can differentiate with respect to time to get

$$da = \frac{2c^2}{\Theta}\left(\frac{a}{a_s}\right)$$

The spin acceleration of the disc is $a = v^2/r = 4\pi^2 R^2 r/3600$ so

$$da = \frac{2c^2}{\Theta}\frac{4\pi^2 R^2 r}{3600a_s}$$

$$da = 2 \times 10^{-10} \times \frac{4\pi^2 \times 18000^2 \times 0.058}{3600 \times 0.03} = 0.0014m/s^2$$

This agrees well with the observation (0.001 m/s²) but unfortunately it does not explain why the anomaly only happens for right spinning discs.

7.24 EMISSION FROM LIGHTNING

The peak wavelength of radiation observed from lightning is about 5 kHz, a wavelength of 60 km[125]. In one case[126] for one part of the atmosphere where lightning was seen, there was a

---

125 Bianchi, C., and A. Meloni, 2009. Natural and man-made terrestrial electromagnetic noise: an outlook. *Annals of Geophysics*, 50(3).

126 Stoltzenberg, M., and T.C, Marshall, 2008. Charge structure and dynamics in thunderstorms. *Space Science Reviews*, 137, 1-4, 355-372.

vertical gradient of 100,000 Volts over a height of 600 metres so the electron acceleration was

$$a = \frac{q_e V}{m_e d} = 2.96 \times 10^{13} m/s^2$$

The wavelength of the Unruh waves emitted should therefore be (combining Unruh's formula with Wien's displacement law)

$$\lambda_U = \frac{4\beta \pi^2 c^2}{a} \sim \frac{8c^2}{a} \sim 24.3 km$$

This is not a million miles from the peak wavelength from the lightning mentioned above, and given the uncertainty it is an interesting result.

This implies that Unruh radiation is connected to electromagnetic radiation, and this has also been suggested by a recent paper which linked the Larmor formula for the radiation of a charged particle with the Unruh radiation expected[127]. This interesting paper is a useful step towards connecting Unruh radiation and QI with the rest of physics.

Unruh radiation has now been directly seen for the first time, using decelerating positrons by Lynch et al.[128], though lightening may provide a shockingly cheap way to look for it.

7.25 THRUST FROM AN ASYMMETRIC CASIMIR EFFECT

The Casimir effect is the force between two parallel plates caused by the void they make in the quantum vacuum. It is like a quantum version of the fact that two ships side by side damp

---

127   Vacalis, G., A. Higutchi, R. Bingham and G. Gregori, 2023. *Phys. Rev. D.*, 109, 024044.

128   Lynch, M.H et al., 2021. *Phys. Rev. D*, 104, 025015

the waves between them and so are pushed together by impacts from waves from outside. The Casimir force is

$$F = \frac{\hbar c \pi^2 A}{240 d^4}$$

where ħ is Planck's constant divided by 2π, c is the speed of light, A is the plates' surface area and d is their separation. Now instead of considering just the zero point field, imagine we put some mass-energy into the space between the plates of the cavity by making electrons accelerate so that they see Unruh radiation. To model this we replace ħ by $E\tau$, where E is the energy applied to the electrons and τ is the time they stay in the cavity

$$\hbar \to E\tau \to \frac{Ed}{v} \to \frac{PQ\tau d}{v} \to \frac{PQd^2}{v^2}$$

where P is the power input, Q is the number of oscillations, reflections or bounces the energy can make in the cavity, and v is the speed of the electrons. The force is now

$$F = \frac{PQ}{c} \frac{c^2}{v^2} \frac{\pi^2}{240} \frac{A}{d^2}$$

This formula gives the force predicted by quantised inertia (QI's first name was: Modified inertia by a Hubble Scale Casimir effect or MiHsC). QI offers a way to utilise the Casimir effect and hugely enhance it by turning the weak zero point field into a stronger Unruh field, using high acceleration.

For example, if we put 1W into a cavity with a quality factor Q of 5, the electrons move at 1% the speed of light, the plate area is 0.01m² and the plate separation is 1 cm, then we get a force of a milliNewton (mN). The best way to boost this would be to take advantage of the squared parameters in the denominator and either use slower moving particles than electrons, or reduce d. Reduce d to 10 micron and the force is 685 N.

7.26 EMDRIVE

The emdrive is an asymmetric radio-frequency resonant cavity shaped like a truncated cone [129] (schematic). The explanation for the apparent thrust from QI is as follows[130]. Microwaves are input by a magnetron and they accelerate back and forth, making an Unruh field shown by the shades of grey. In a similar way to the Casimir effect, at the wide end

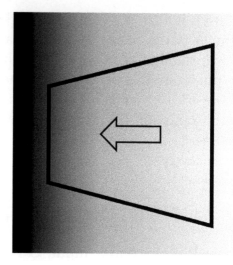

Figure 74. An emdrive with its Unruh background.

more of these Unruh wavelengths can exist so the photons see an intense (many allowed waves) Unruh field (light shade) and they have a larger inertial mass. At the narrow end fewer Unruh waves can fit so the photons see a colder field (dark) and have less inertia. One way to understand the QI thrust is that the continual shift of inertia towards the wide end must be compensated by the cavity moving towards its narrow end.

---

129 Shawyer, R, 2008. Microwave propulsion—progress in the emdrive programme. 59th International Astronautical Conference. IAC-2008. Glasgow, UK.

130 McCulloch, 2017. Testing quantised inertia on emdrives with dielectrics. *EPL*, 118, 34003.

Another way to see it is that the gradient in the Unruh field pushes the cavity left.

In the emdrive (Shawyer's model 2, chosen here for its simplicity & lack of a dielectric) the power input was 1000 W. The Q factor for the microwaves was 45,000. So, crudely ignoring the shape for now we get

$$F = \frac{1000 \times 45000}{3 \times 10^8} \frac{(3 \times 10^8)^2}{(3 \times 10^8)^2} \frac{\pi^2}{240} \frac{0.3^2}{0.3^2} = 6.2mN$$

The observed thrust was between 80 and 204 mN but when we take account of the tapered shape of the emdrive, QI gives good predictions of the thrusts seen in the eleven tests done so far (a good 149 mN for this case, see reference 130), and QI also predicts that you can get a much higher thrust if you optimise the shape, for example by varying the slope of the walls and by placing a dielectric at the wide end.

7.27 WOODWARD 'MACH EFFECT' THRUSTER

The Mach Effect thruster in the experiment here[131] consists of a stack of four lead zirconium titanate capacitors, each 1.9 cm in diameter and 0.19 cm thick (the grey rectangles in the schematic). The black areas in the schematic are aluminium end caps. The one on the left was much thicker. The thrust was determined by motion.

From a QI standpoint, the thin end cap on the right does not damp Unruh waves, so we have a lot of wavelengths there, the light shade in the schematic. The thick end damps the Unruh waves, allowing fewer Unruh waves, the darker shade. This will make a gradient in the Unruh background that will push the system towards the thick plate, as observed. Again,

---

131 Mahood, 1999. STAIF-2000. 1014-20

an asymmetric Casimir effect so we can use the same formula

$$F = \frac{PQ}{c} \frac{c^2}{v^2} \frac{\pi^2}{240} \frac{A}{d^2}$$

The value of Q is not known for this case, but for a similar test the Q was 60^{132}. The input power was 145W. The predicted thrust from QI is

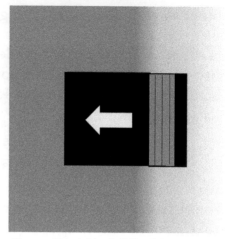

Figure 75. A Mach Effect thruster with its Unruh background (greyscale).

$$F = \frac{145 \times 60}{3 \times 10^8} \frac{(3 \times 10^8)^2}{(3 \times 10^8)^2} \frac{\pi^2}{240} \frac{0.0003}{0.0076^2} = 0.006mN$$

The observed thrust from the experiment was 0.05mN. The prediction is therefore a factor of eight out.

7.28 ASYMMETRIC CAPACITORS

NASA[133] tested an asymmetric capacitor in a vacuum, charging it up to 44kV with a leakage current of 5mA. The power input was less than 220W, the plate separation was 6.35 cm and the plates were 3 cm in diameter. Whenever a discharge occurred the capacitor moved with a force of 14 mN. This was not due to ion drift or recoil from an evaporation of the metal plates because no erosion of the plates was seen, and it would have been.

132   March and Palfreyman, 2006. STAIF 2006, 1321–1332.

133   Martins A.A., and M.J. Pinheiro, 2011. On the propulsive force developed by an asymmetric capacitors in a vacuum. SPESIF-2011. *Physics Procedia*, 20, 112-119.

Again, QI explains it because the thick plate blocks more Unruh waves, see the schematic, so the capacitor again moves down the Unruh gradient (light->dark), or if you like, towards the horizon (the thick plate).

As above, we can use the equation

Figure 76. An asymmetric capacitor with its Unruh background (greyscale).

$$F = \frac{PQ}{c} \frac{c^2}{v^2} \frac{\pi^2}{240} \frac{A}{d^2}$$

The quality factor of a cavity is $Q = 2\pi f E/P = \pi c \varepsilon A V^2/Pd^2 = 16{,}587$ (using $E = \frac{1}{2}CV^2$, $f = c/d$ and $C = \varepsilon A/d$). We are now dealing with accelerated electrons and their acceleration from plate to plate was $a = q_e V/m_e d$ so their final speed across the gap was $v = at = q_e Vt/m_e d = q_e V/(m_e(v/2))$ ($v/2$ is the average speed across the gap). So that $v^2 = 2q_e V/m_e)$ and their average speed is half that, so $v = \frac{1}{2}(2q_e V/m_e)^{1/2} = 21\%$ of c.

$$F = \frac{220 \times 16587}{3x10^8} \frac{1^2}{0.21^2} \frac{\pi^2}{240} \frac{0.03^2}{0.0625^2} = 2.6mN$$

The observed thrust was 14 mN. QI predicts that the thrust should be towards the thicker capacitor plate. The observed direction was not reported but was inferred to be that way.

7.29 SYMMETRIC CAPACITORS

It was observed by [134],[135] and especially[136] that capacitors with dielectrics between the plates (or air) which are so charged up that they approach the dielectric's breakdown voltage, show thrust towards their anodes.

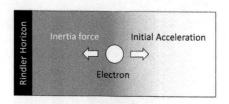

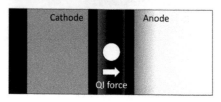

Figure 77. Empty space & a symmetric capacitor with their Unruh background.

The upper panel shows that in open space, in quantised inertia, an accelerated electron sees more Unruh radiation in front (the light-grey area) because there is no horizon nearby damping it, and less Unruh radiation behind (the dark grey area) because it is damped by the Rindler horizon (the black area). So, the electron sees a radiation imbalance pushing it back against its acceleration and this explains why it has inertia.[137]

The lower panel shows the situation in the capacitor. The electrons are accelerated to the right by a potential difference between the plates. Again they see a Rindler horizon, shown on the left by the vertical black line. The electrons will see Unruh waves, but these will be deselected as electrons will move to cancel the electromagnetic (Unruh) fields between the capacitor

134 Canning, F.X., C. Melcher, W. Winet, 2004. NASA/CR-2004-213312.

135 Musha, T., 2008. *JBIS*, 61, 379-384.

136 Becker, F.M. and A.S. Bhatt, 2018. Arxiv: https://arxiv.org/abs/1810.04368

137 McCulloch, M.E., 2013. *EPL*, 101, 59001.

plates (the black area) so that the normal gradient is reversed and now there are more Unruh waves behind (the dark grey area) so the electrons get an extra kick forward. In a sense the electrons' inertial mass has been reversed.

As in section 7.25 we can model this by replacing the units of Joule seconds ($\hbar$) in the Casimir effect by the energy-time we are putting in electrically. The assumption is that all this energy accelerates the electrons, and ends up as Unruh radiation which is then damped between the plates

$$\hbar \to E\tau \to \frac{Ed}{v} \to \frac{P\tau d}{v} \to \frac{Pd^2}{v^2}$$

where E is the energy between the plates, τ is the time it stays between the plates and P is the power applied. The electrons' acceleration from plate to plate is $a = q_e V/m_e d$ so as calculated in section 7.28 their average speed is $v = \frac{1}{2}(2q_e V/m_e)^{1/2}$ and

$$\hbar = \frac{2Pd^2m_e}{q_e V}$$

So the force is

$$F = \frac{2Pd^2m_e}{q_e V}\frac{c\pi^2 A}{240d^4}$$

Since P=IV we have

$$F = \frac{0.082 \times IAm_e c}{q_e d^2} \sim \frac{0.000141IA}{d^2}$$

This is the thrust predicted by quantised inertia[138] and will be transmitted by electron impacts to the anode and the

138 McCulloch, M.E, 2021. Research Gate. Thrust from Symmetric Capacitors using Quantised Inertia. DOI:10.13140/RG.2.2.16916.01921

capacitor's structure. The electron acceleration occurs as the electron passes between the plates. Note that the equation above has no arbitrary parameters, the 0.00014 comes from known values of the mass and charge of the electron and the speed of light.

One can also think of this process, with the same maths, as a loss of inertia (ie momentum) by the electrons between the plates (as Unruh waves are disallowed) which must be compensated by a gain of momentum by the whole capacitor towards the anode, accounting for the thrust.

The graph below shows a comparison between the experiment done by Becker and Bhatt described here[139] and the QI prediction. The black diamonds show the observed thrust in Newtons on the y axis as a function of the separation of the capacitor plates on the x axis in metres. The error bars are also shown. The predictions from quantised inertia are shown as open squares & agree within the error bars with the data.

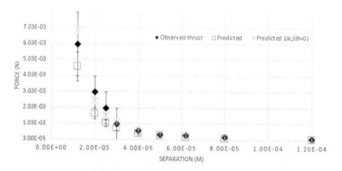

OBSERVED THRUST & THAT PREDICTED BY QI

Figure 78. Capacitor thrust (y axis, Newtons) & plate separation (x axis, metres) as observed by Becker & Bhatt (2018) (the black diamonds) & as predicted by QI (the open squares).

---

139 Becker, F. and A. Bhatt, 2018. Electrostatic accelerated electrons within symmetric capacitors during field emission condition events exert bidirectional propellant-less thrust. https://arxiv.org/abs/1810.04368

It can be seen that happily the thrust increases exponentially as the plate separation is reduced and the largest force (on the left) was about 6mN. The tests showed that heating to 50°C is also required to encourage electrons to overcome the metal's work function & jump the gap, so if we assume 1W of heating then the thrust to power ratio is 6 N/kW which is about 300 times better than the ion drives currently used in satellites.

A reasonable mass for a solar electric power system is 20 kg/kW. A 1 kW unit could be included in a 60 kg spacecraft. At a thrust/power ratio of 6 N/kW, 6 N of thrust would be available, accelerating the spacecraft at a rate of 0.1 m/s². The velocity change required to travel from a Low Earth Orbit (LEO) to Geosynchronous orbit on a low thrust trajectory is 5000 m/s. Accordingly a spacecraft so equipped would be able to do the transfer in 50,000 s, or roughly 14 hours. This is almost as fast as that enabled by a high thrust chemical rocket transfer stage. The latter however, would require an amount of propellant roughly triple the mass of the spacecraft, which would greatly increase the launch cost, not to mention the cost of the upper stage itself. Much larger benefits would follow from using such a thruster on more ambitious missions. The velocity change to go from LEO to solar system escape velocity is 20 km/s. The above-described spacecraft could execute that manoeuvre in 55 hours.[140]

If a thruster was built using a Lithium-air battery capable of 1.8kW/kg then an upwards force of 10.8N could be achieved, not too far from the downwards force from the battery (1kg=10N) and thruster (a weight of up to 1kg = 10N). QI predicts that the best way to enhance the thrust would be to reduce the separation of the plates or increase their area.

---

140 Thanks to my editor (RZ) for this example.

7.30 MODDEL'S CASIMIR CAVITY

It has been argued[141] that if an asymmetric arrangement of metal plates was built on the nanoscale then it could produce thrust with no power. The metal structure would damp the vacuum asymmetrically and the structure would 'fall down' the vacuum gradient.

Such a structure has recently been built by Moddel[142]. It consisted of a lower palladium plate about 33 nm thick (see the schematic). A 2 nm thick insulator above it across which electrons can 'tunnel' to and from a thinner upper palladium plate, 10 nm thick. Above that plate was a transparent dielectric layer (it varied between 33 and 1000 nm thick) and above that an aluminium mirror, 150 nm thick. The electrons may have tunnelled across the 2 nm insulator gap at an acceleration of $10^{25}ms^{-2}$ so the quantum vacuum should have been enhanced by Unruh radiation short enough (their wavelength is $8c^2/a =$ 72nm) to interact with the metal structure—the grey shades shown in the background. The upper dielectric and mirror form a Casimir cavity which damps the quantum vacuum (the dark band) and, according to quantised inertia should produce a force upwards (white arrow).

Indeed, even when there was no driving voltage difference, this structure produced a current of electrons from the lower palladium plate to the upper. Also, as predicted, the current increased as the Casimir cavity was made thinner, as more Unruh waves are damped. When it was 33 nm thick, the observed current was 60 nA = 60 nC/s. This implies that there were N_e = 3.8×10^{11} electrons crossing per second. The observed mass flux of electrons was then 3.4×10$^{-19}kg/s$.

141   McCulloch, M.E., 2020. Can nanocavities push off the quantum vacuum? *Progress in Physics*, 16, 2, 92-93.

142   Moddel, G., A. Weerakkody, D. Doroski, D. Bartusiak, 2021. Optical cavity induced current. *Symmetry*, 13, 517.

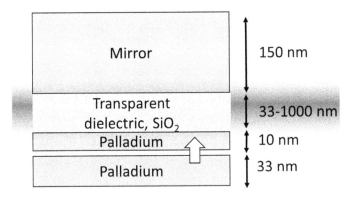

Figure 79. Moddel's Casimir cavity.

We can calculate this, again from the uncertainty principle, as in Section 6.6, but assuming as usual that QI determines that Δx is the distance to the horizon (here, a solid boundary). So

$$\Delta p = \frac{\hbar}{2\Delta x} = \Delta(mc)$$

Therefore, the flux of mass with respect to time is as follows, where we assume that $\Delta x = 33$ nm–the distance across the dielectric, and c is the speed of light in the dielectric (0.5c, a rough estimate).

$$\frac{\Delta m}{\Delta t} = \frac{\hbar}{c\Delta x\Delta t} = \frac{\hbar}{(\Delta x)^2} = 0.9 \times 10^{-19} kg/s$$

The prediction is about a third of the observed mass flux per second. This is acceptable given the crudeness of the approximations. QI also predicts the increase of the force seen when the dielectric was narrowed.[143]

---

143   The force is tiny: F = dp/dt = d(mc)/dt = c.Δm/Δt = 2.7 × 10^{-11}N but it is applied to electrons, which have a very small mass. Hence the current.

This could be a form of propulsion that does not need propellant or indeed even the input of energy. The acceleration of the structure is of course tiny and the photoinjector was fixed so it was never going to leap off the bench and through a wall (like the device in the film Explorers), but the point is that this is thrust from the vacuum: a new source, and cheaper.

The quantum vacuum has no energy until it has a gradient in it. We know that because if it did, the mass-energy would act gravitationally and the cosmos would be shrunk to the size of the Moon's orbit[144] However, and assumed in QI, with a gradient the vacuum can produce workable energy, hence the Casimir effect and the examples discussed in this book.

7.31 PODKLETNOV'S DISC.

Podkletnov[145] levitated a ceramic disc whose upper half was superconducting at 70K with crystals of size $2\mu m$ and a non-superconducting lower half with crystals of size $10\mu m$. He also applied an AC (alternating) magnetic field (2 Tesla & $10^8\,Hz$) and noticed that objects of all kinds placed above the disc lost 0.05% in weight.

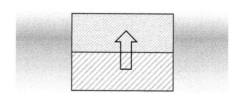

Figure 80. Podkletnov's Disc.

---

144 Nernst, W. 1921. Das Weltgebäude im Lichte der Neueren Forschung. Berlin: Julius Springer. Discussed in H. Kragh, Preludes to dark energy: Zero-point energy and vacuum speculations

145 Podkletnov, E.E. and R. Nieminen, 1992. A possibility of gravitational shielding by bulk YBa2Cu3O7-x superconductor. *Physica C*, 203, 441-444.

The effect did not appear for fully superconducting discs, so the two layers were crucial. The effect occurred in vacuum and the AC magnetic field was essential.

QI predicts that a structure with a cavity size that varies will produce a gradient in the quantum vacuum as fine grains will damp Unruh radiation more as fewer waves are allowed (see shades) the gradient will then push on it[146]. The QI force for an array of cavities length L & l (smaller) is

$$F = \frac{\hbar c}{(L + l)} \left(\frac{1}{l} - \frac{1}{L} \right)$$

For a large cavity of 10µm and a small cavity of 2µm we have l=L/5 so

$$F = \frac{10\hbar c}{3L^2}$$

This force is being applied within the material to each cell of size $2\mu m$ or $10\mu m$ so the net force is a balance between gravity acting down (ρ=density) and a force upwards due to QI. So assuming $L = 5\mu m$ as an average.

$$F = \frac{10\hbar c}{3L^2} - \rho L^3 g = 4 \times 10^{-15} - 2.5 \times 10^{-12} \text{ N}$$

The positive (upwards) force is 0.16% of the gravitational. The observed loss of weight was 0.05%. The problem here is that the theory assumes only the quantum vacuum, but the effect also needed an AC magnetic field.

---

146 McCulloch, 2020. Can nanocavities push off the quantum vacuum? *Progress in Physics*, 16, 2, 92-93.

7.32 PODKLETNOV'S IMPULSATOR

Not satisfied with the furore created by his disc, Podkletnov made an Impulsator[147]. It has two superconducting electrodes. A metal sphere of radius 0.5 m, coated with a superconducting ceramic (see the left hand side of the schematic). Another electrode was placed 0.2 metres away (the black circle). A current of 10,000A was applied and the voltage difference

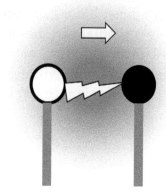

Figure 81. Podkletnov's Impulsator.

was 1MV (more powerful than your average van der Graaf generator). This is a power of 10GW. A discharge occurred between the two electrodes (orange spark) and an impulse was seen that propagated to the right, and knocked over objects in adjoining rooms. The force of the impulse was proportional to the mass of the objects and independent of their composition, implying an inertial effect.

The force produced was also proportional to the voltage squared, at least below 1kV, as predicted in section 7.28 where Q is proportional to V^2 (for the data see Table 1 and 2 in the first footnote below). An explanation from QI could be that the high voltage enhances the quantum vacuum in the locality (the light areas in the schematic) but the spheres damp it between them as in a capacitor. The zone of low Unruh radiation (dark circle) moves to the right. When it strikes a target, it produces

---

147 Podkletnov, E., G. Modanese, 2001. https://arxiv.org/abs/physics/0108005

a gradient in Unruh radiation on that target that pushes on it. We can use the QI formula[148] published in[149]

$$F = \frac{\pi \varepsilon A V^2}{L^2} = \frac{\pi \times 8.85 \times 10^{-12} \times \pi \times 0.25^2 \times 2000000^2}{0.2^2} = 546N$$

The observed force was estimated by Podkletnov to be 10,000N for 2000kV but this estimate was very approximate and was dependent on a time constant that Podkletnov assumed to be 0.001s, without any data.

7.33 BALL LIGHTNING

Ball lightning is a well-observed phenomenon in which lightning produces a coherent ball of light that hovers over the ground, lasts for several minutes and then explodes or dissipates. It has been suggested that it could be explained as a microwave cavity—microwaves trapped in a ball. QI offers a way to explain the trapping. Let us assume that it is a plasma and the electrons collect on the plasma's surface and repel each other according to Coulomb's law. The force between two electrons at the edge of the ball, assuming they are separated by 4 nanometres (from the density of air), is

$$F = \frac{q^2}{4\pi\varepsilon_0 r^2} = 0.01nN$$

So why does the ball not just explode? What if the plasma inside the ball acts like the metal in the asymmetric capacitor? The ions (the mottled area) are able to freely move and

---

148   ε = the permittivity of free space (F/m), A = plate area (m²), V = voltage, L = separation (m).

149   McCulloch, M.E., 2018. Propellant-less propulsion from quantised inertia. *J. Space Expl.*, 7, 3, 151-

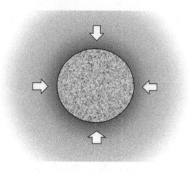

Figure 82. A Ball of Plasma.

cancel any electromagnetic field associated with the quantum background leaving a supervoid (the dark area à). As above, we can model the force inwards assuming that the power involved is, as described, similar to a 20 Watt bulb (based on eyewitness accounts of brightness). It is unclear what the Q factor is here. How many times can electromagnetic waves bounce around inside? Q could be anything above 1, so we can only predict a range for the force:

$$F > \frac{PQ}{c} > \frac{20 \times 1}{3 \times 10^8} > 67nN$$

For any value of Q, this force would counter the plasma explosion (0.01 nN) and keep the ball intact. However, what I was hoping for here was a close balance, which this is not.

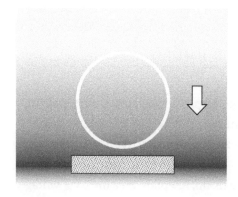

Figure 83. A laser loop with damper.

7.34 PHOTON THRUST

Something that has become clear through experiments is that to extract QI thrust it can be better to use heavy electrons. Accelerating light can work (emdrive), but photons are rather (ahem) light, and you need more power.

The schematic shows one such setup that we tried[150]. A fibre optic loop (white), carried laser light (power = 0.129 Watts) and enforced a high acceleration on the photons to enhance the Unruh quantum background that the photons see (the light background area in the schematic), except below where the metal scale pan (dotted) damped the Unruh field producing the low energy (darker) area. The loop is then pushed down by the Unruh gradient.

We can use the same formula as for the other thrusters, ie

$$F = \frac{PQ}{c} \frac{c^2}{v^2} \frac{\pi^2}{240} \frac{A}{d^2}$$

With an estimated Q=300, A=0.01 m² & d = 1 cm, this predicts a thrust of

$$F = \frac{0.129 \times 300}{c} \frac{c^2}{v^2} \frac{\pi^2}{240} \frac{A}{d^2} = 1.1\mu N$$

Please note, that the 'c' in the equation above is the speed of light in the fibre, typically v=0.7c for glass. This is a very small force, not measurable and much smaller than the thrust you can get by accelerating electrons with capacitors, which is on the order of mN, ie: 1000 times larger.[151] The emdrive used microwaves, true, but of a much higher power and Q factor.

7.35 DYNAMICAL CASIMIR EFFECT

If you thought the Casimir effect was cool, and I do, then just wait till you hear about the Dynamical Casimir effect. This was

---

150 Experiment tried by a collaborator Prof Jose Perez-Diaz, at the University of Alcala in Madrid.

151 This may also explain the negative tests of photon cavities by Neunzig et al., 2021. CEAS Space Journal. Doi: 10.1007/s12567-021-00366-4

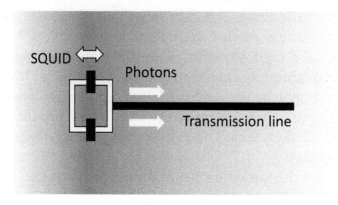

Figure 84. The Wilson Experiment.

first produced in a lab in 2011 by Wilson et al [152] who set up a transmission line with a SQUID (Superconducting Quantum Interference Device) on the end (see diagram). The SQUID's inductance (an induced voltage caused by a change in the current) can be varied quickly by applying a magnetic field to it. This varies the effective electrical length of the transmission line (the horizontal black line), in this case at a frequency (f_d) of 10 GHz and with a speed (v) of 10% the speed of light. This is equivalent to moving a mirror at this same speed, since screening currents move through the SQUID in the same way that electrons move in a metal, a mirror, or plasma, to damp the zero point field.

The normal Casimir effect works because the two plates enforce nodes in the quantum vacuum and so damp (reduce) it. This moving 'mirror' also forces nodes in the vacuum as it 'moves', damping it. This is the reason for the dark vertical band in the schematic representing low Unruh intensity. In the experiment they detected photons being emitted from the

---

152   Wilson et al., 2011. Observation of the dynamical Casimir effect in a superconducting circuit. *Nature*. 479, 376–379.

vacuum at a wavelength of 0.4 m or 750 MHz (see the white arrows on the schematic).

How does this tally with Unruh radiation and quantised inertia? The acceleration of the horizon formed by the SQUID is

$$a = \frac{2v}{t} = 2vf_a = 2 \times (0.1 \times 3 \times 10^8) \times (10 \times 10^9) = 6 \times 10^{17} m/s^2$$

The Unruh wavelength such an acceleration would see is given by

$$\lambda_U = \frac{2c^2}{a} = 0.3m$$

This is close to the radiation that was seen to be emitted (which was 0.4m) so it may have been Unruh radiation. The radiation was all emitted in one direction (to the right in the schematic) which opens up the possibility of using this to produce photon thrust.

As reported in the Wilson paper, the power output of the device at a pump power of 100pW (picoWatt) was about 12 photon.s^{-1}Hz^{-1}, so at 10 GHz it would be 120 $\times$ 10^9 photons per second. Each photon has an energy of $E = hf_d$ so the power emitted is the energy times the number of photons per second

$$P = hf_d \times 120 \times 10^9 = 7.9 \times 10^{-13} W$$

The thrust obtainable from this power is F=P/c=2.7×10^{-21}N. The thrust to power ratio here is 3.3 $\times$ 10^{-9} N/kW. Very small, but if we could increase the frequency of the SQUID by a factor of a million then we would have something close to an ion drive (0.02 N/kW) without needing fuel.

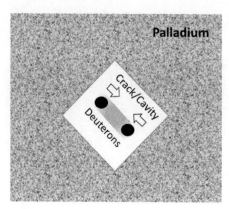

Figure 85. Unruh radiation in a metal defect.

7.36 LENR/COLD FUSION

QI offers an explanation for cold fusion by assuming that in Heisenberg's formula, $\Delta p \Delta x > \hbar/2$, the Δx is determined by the size of a cavity and the Δp becomes real momentum[153]. The schematic shows two highly accelerated deuterons (the black circles) close together inside a defect/cavity (full from their accelerated viewpoint of intense, white, Unruh radiation) within a palladium lattice (the mottled area). There will be a mutual sheltering process (see the darker Unruh-radiation-free area) and so there will be a radiation recoil force that will push them together (the white arrows). The new energy in the cavity is given by

$$\Delta E > \frac{\hbar c}{2D}$$

For thermalised energy $E = {}^3/_2 kT$ so

$$T > \frac{\hbar c}{3kD}$$

If the temperature within the defect is as given by the equation above then this radiation will be absorbed by each deuteron only on the side away from the other deuteron, assuming there is a mutual sheltering process (see the dark radiation-free area)

153 McCulloch, M.E., 2018. Can cold fusion be explained by quantised inertia? *Progress in Physics*, 14, 2, 63-65.

and so the absorption of this radiation will produce a radiation recoil that will push them together. This force is

$$F_R = \frac{P}{c} = \frac{\sigma T^4}{c}$$

Where P is power, σ is the Stefan-Boltzmann constant and c is the speed of light. In order for this radiative force to cause the deuterons to fuse, it must be larger than the repulsive Coulomb force F_C at the separation where the attractive strong force can take over and fuse the two deuterons, a distance of $d_s = 1.6\times10^{-15}m$. For this to happen, $F_R > F_C$ at distance d_s, and so using the equations above, the Coulumb equation for repulsion and a bit of algebra, QI predicts the crack size, D, needed to produce a temperature high enough to cause fusion in this new way

$$D < (4\pi\varepsilon_0\sigma)^{1/4}c^{3/4}\frac{\hbar}{3k}\sqrt{\frac{d_s}{q}} = 28nm$$

So, if there are defects in palladium of a size of 28 nm or less, then QI predicts there will be temperatures of ~$\hbar c/3kD \geq$ 25,900K, deuterons will be pushed together by Unruh radiation in the crack strongly enough that their Coulomb barrier can be breached, causing fusion. Cracks of this size are present in palladium, after being stressed[154].

Cold fusion & LENR have often been called 'crackpot' science, which may be true, just not in the way they think. Cracks may indeed be the key to it!

---

154 Kim, S., H.-S, Lee, B. Jang and S. Cho., 2016. *J. Mater. Sci.,* 51(9), 4530-4537.

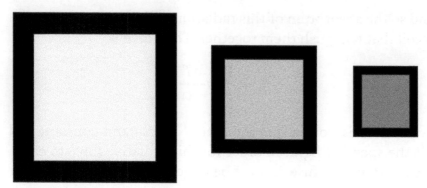

Figure 86. Unruh radiation in a vari-sized boxes.

7.37 LIGHT FROM NANOCAVITIES

The Planck limit should limit the power emitted from a hot body to $P = \sigma T^4$ where σ is the Stefan-Boltzmann constant[155] and T is the absolute temperature. In this experiment[156], photonic crystals were heated to 600K so the power emission should have been 7.4kW/m². They measured eight times the expected power, about 60kW/m². Where does all this extra energy come from?

As discussed above, quantised inertia predicts that the quantum vacuum contained within a metal box of size D will have a temperature of ($\hbar c/3kD$). In other words, smaller metal boxes will have a higher temperature and this energy will originate solely from the vacuum. See the shades in the schematic (white = hotter, dark = cooler).

In the experiment, the photonic crystals were formed by tungsten rods spaced by about $1\mu m$. QI predicts that the power emitted by the photonic crystals, for a box size of D (in this case $1\mu m$) is

---

155 The Stephen-Boltzmann constant, $\sigma = 5.67 \times 10^{-8}$ W m^{-2} K^{-4}

156 Lin et al., 2020. Super-Planckian Thermal Radiation Emitted From a Metallic Photonic-Crystal at Optical Wavelengths. *Sci. Rep.*, 10, 5209.

$$P = \sigma \left(\frac{\hbar c}{3kD} \right)^4 = 15.4 kW/m^2$$

The observed emission was 60 kW/m². If this power could be channelled in one direction, as in this experiment, it leads to a thrust, for a one metre squared thruster, of $F = P/c = 51\mu N$. The equation above shows that you can enhance this by using smaller cavities.

7.38 STAR IN A JAR

Single-bubble sonoluminescence is a phenomenon seen in acoustically-driven distilled water contained in glass spheres. Under the focussed sound, a central bubble (see schematic) repeatedly collapses with a well-documented flash of light (see the white star). The spectrum of this light implies that the temperature of the bubble upon collapse to a diameter of 0.5 micron is between 2300K and 5100K (see the circle).

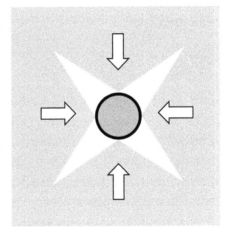

Figure 87. The sonoluminescent flash.

As in the section on nanocavities above, quantised inertia predicts that a restriction of space should release real energy and heat from the quantum vacuum. Using the equation for temperature in the sections on cold fusion (7.36) and nanocavities (7.37), we can estimate the temperature of the bubble when it reaches 0.5 micron, as

$$T > \frac{\hbar c}{3kD} > 1449K$$

Given the uncertainty in the measurements, this is roughly the right size but it is true that there are many other proposed explanations for sonoluminescence[157] such as high pressures or ionisation causing high temperatures and light emission, so I include it here merely as a possibility that happens to fit.

Sonoluminescence is nevertheless a fascinating phenomenon, used for example by pistol shrimp to launch bubbles that can kill small fish, and so it can be forgiven for being a tax on one's spelling.

7.39 NANOSPHERE SPIN

Arita et al.[158] suspended a microsphere of radius 2.2×10^{-6} *metres* on a laser beam, and polarised the beam to spin it at up to 600,000,000 rpm. This spin produces an acceleration of the microsphere with respect to its surroundings and QI predicts that its inertial mass should increase. This means it should become less responsive to the Earth's gravity, and to conserve momentum in the vertical direction it should accelerate upwards anomalously. QI can predict the spin rate needed to produce an upwards acceleration greater than the downwards acceleration of gravity.

The initial acceleration (a_s) is the mutual acceleration of the microsphere with respect to the fixed stars since it is on the rotating Earth. At the latitude of St Andrews, Scotland, where the experiment was done, this acceleration is $a_s = v^2/r$, where r is the distance from the Earth's spin axis ($r = r_0 cos\phi$ where r_0

---

157 Brenner M.P., S. Hingenfeldt & D. Lohse, 2002. *Rev. Mod. Phys.*, 7492, 425-484.

158 Arita et al., 2013. *Nature Communications*. DOI: 10.1038/ncomms3374

is the earth's radius: 6367500m and ϕ is the latitude of 53.34 degrees). The velocity $v = 2\pi r/86400$. So $a_s = 4\pi^2 r_0 \cos\phi/86400^2 = 0.02 m/s^2$.

The mutual acceleration between the microsphere and surrounding matter when it is spun, at a radius from the spin axis of the microsphere of r, is

$$a_r = \frac{4\pi^2 R^2 r}{3600}$$

where R is the revolutions per minute (rpm). To get the average acceleration of all the matter in the microsphere (which is what matters in quantised inertia) we divide by Pi and then substitute the equation above into the equation we used for the flybys (7.20). The anomalous upwards acceleration for the microsphere is

$$da = \frac{2c^2}{\Theta} \frac{4\pi R^2 r}{3600 a_s} \sim 0.7 \times 10^{-12} \times \frac{R^2 r}{a_s}$$

Using this we can predict the rotation rate (in rpm) needed to produce an upwards anomalous acceleration by quantised inertia for the microsphere that is able to oppose gravity (R_{crit}) by setting $da = g \sim 9.8 m/s^2$ as follows

$$R_{crit} = \sqrt{\frac{450 g a_s \Theta}{c^2 \pi r}} = \sqrt{\frac{450 \times 9.8 \times 0.02 \times 8.8 \times 10^{26}}{(3 \times 10^8)^2 \times \pi \times 2.2 \times 10^{-6}}} = 3.5 \times 10^8 rpm$$

In their experiment they found that the spinning microspheres 'disappeared' (ie: escaped from the laser light trap in a manner that is not yet clear) at rotation rates of around 6 × $10^8 rpm$ which is not far from the critical rotation rate predicted by quantised inertia.

Of course, in this case the disappearance of the microsphere could be due to standard physics—ie: it could have centrifugally exploded!—and this is being investigated (K. Dholakia, pers. comm.) but QI could also be a potential cause.

One way to test this would be to observe the microsphere around the critical rotation rate to see if it moves upwards, and also try the same experiment for different values of the sphere radius (r) and see if $R_{crit} = \sqrt{1/r}$ as predicted here.

7.40 PAIR PRODUCTION

Pair production occurs when a photon of sufficient energy approaches a nucleus and turns into an electron and a positron[159]. The process can be modelled as the scattering of a photon by the nucleus using quantum mechanics but this is rather complex[160]. Quantised inertia offers an alternative, nicely illustrative and simpler mechanism.

The schematic shows a photon (grey curve) passing by an atomic nucleus (black circle). We assume that the photon is trying to dissipate into an electron and a positron all the time: photon vortices of opposite rotation that appear on either side of it. These are shown by the curved black arrows. The orientation of the photons'

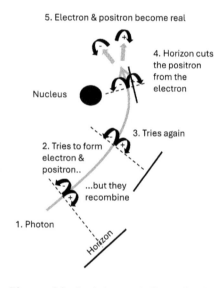

Figure 88. An interpretation of pair production.

(labels in figure:) 5. Electron & positron become real · 4. Horizon cuts the positron from the electron · Nucleus · 3. Tries again · 2. Tries to form electron & positron.. · ...but they recombine · 1. Photon · Horizon

---

159   Blackett & Occhialini, 1933. *Proc. R. Soc. London*, A 139, 839, 699-726.

160   Bethe and Heitler, 1934. *Proc. Phys. Soc. Lond.* 146, 83 112.

tight curve makes them negatively or positively charged, and the electron (negatively charged, anticlockwise spin) must appear closer to the positively charged nucleus. The problem is that these oppositely charged particles will attract, so they will recombine and won't last long. The only way that they can be separated and appear as real is if a horizon can separate them, as happens to produce Hawking or Unruh radiation. Let us now calculate the conditions needed to do this.

As the photon (potential electron and positron) approaches the atom–see the trajectory in the schematic, its acceleration increases. Here, I am assuming the electron is attracted by the positive nucleus (here shown just as a proton) and so the Rindler horizon (thick dashed lines) gets closer. When the horizon is closer to the centroid of the photon than the electron/positron radius, see the upper pair, then the electron no longer 'knows' about the positron, so they can separate. The distance to the Rindler horizon to achieve this (d_R) must be the electron radius and the horizon distance is c^2/a, where 'a' is the photon's acceleration.

$$d_R = r_e = \frac{c^2}{a}$$

The acceleration needed to do this must come from the Coulomb force between the electron and the nucleus (proton)–the positron is further away but will have some effect which is neglected here.

$$a = \frac{c^2}{r_e} = \frac{q^2}{4\pi\varepsilon_0 r_e^2 m_e} = \frac{F}{m}$$

So

$$r_e = \frac{q^2}{4\pi\varepsilon_0 m_e c^2} = 2.814 \times 10^{-15} m$$

The observed charge radius of the electron is $2.818 \times 10^{-15}m$. Note, that since the photon is travelling at the speed of light, the electron and positron will form with a speed predominantly in the same direction, ie: they will be emitted almost co-linearly, as observed.

CHAPTER 8

INTERLUDE: ENERGETICS OF QI

8.1 MAXWELL'S DEMON

I like James Clerk Maxwell. It's difficult not to like someone who used to be called "dafty". Maxwell took the observations of electromagnetism assembled over many years by Michael Faraday, another appealingly humble character, and wrote down equations showing how the electric and magnetic fields played off each other, and showed that their interaction implied a speed for the propagation of the resulting wave that looked suspiciously like the speed of light. That's all nice and mainstream, but Maxwell also dipped into a lot of other fields and helped to create the early understanding of information with his paradox, usually called Maxwell's demon.

Maxwell considered arbitrary particles milling around in a box, as shown here. The box had a removable partition in the middle of it.

These particles would have a varied range of velocities and hence kinetic energies, and Maxwell considered what would happen if an intelligent entity, that was dubbed a 'demon', was able to watch the balls moving around in both halves of the box, then, whenever Mr Demon saw a fast moving particle in the left half going right, he would be able to open the partition for an instant and let it pass from the left half to the right.

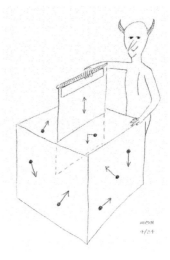

Eventually, using the information he had about the balls and their speeds the demon would be able to do this repeatedly so that all the fast balls would be in the right-hand half of the box. What has happened is that information has allowed an intelligence to reduce the entropy of the system. With all the fast moving particles (ie: heat) on the right hand side, the box is now more ordered than

Figure 89. Maxwell's Demon at work.

it was before—its entropy has decreased, so the Second Law of Thermodynamics is not happy. Also, whereas beforehand no energy could be extracted from the random distribution of energy in the box, now it would be possible to put a fan blade & dynamo in a hole in the partition, and allow the faster molecules on one side to flow through it, and rotate it. This is energy from information.

The inexorable increase in entropy has been reversed and energy created from nothing by this intelligence. It is no wonder they called it a demon, since it upset just about all of thermodynamics and physical law at the time.

8.2 SZILARD'S ENGINE

In the 20th Century Leo Szilard realised what a horrendous problem Maxwell's demon was for physics, because if it was true then you would have a perpetual motion machine. All the demon would have to do is continue to dynamically select molecules and make a door in the partition with a rotor in it to extract energy from the escape of the faster molecules.

This reminds me of the development of thermodynamics in about 1800. Count Rumford showed that when a screw is turned in water, the water warms up: heat energy was apparently being generated out of nowhere, until it was realised that heat was just the agitation of molecules on tiny scales and not due to some magical substance called phlogiston that was created by friction. Similarly, with Szilard's Engine we are getting energy apparently out of nothing. To solve the problem, you just have to appreciate that information is something real, like microscopic motion, that can be converted to energy.

Szilard realised that information is never free and proposed that as the demon does work looking at the molecules to determine their positions and speeds, he releases heat. This was essential to maintain the 2nd law of thermodynamics which states that entropy (the amount of energy in an unusable form, eg: heat) must never decrease. It may well be true that Maxwell's Demon can decrease the entropy within the box by making the right hot and the left colder, but the process he uses to do so, releases heat so that the overall temperature of the cosmos and its entropy increases to compensate for the decrease in entropy in the box.

Szilard's point was that every time a bit of information was used by the demon the entropy would increase by k times log2 where k is Boltzmann's constant.

But this was not yet very clear. Exactly when in the process was heat being released to save the second law of thermodynamics?

8.3 LANDAUER'S PRINCIPLE

The paradox was resolved in 1961 by Rolf Landauer[161] [162]who was working at IBM and studying computer memory. He realised that a computer's memory is not just the 0s and 1s we see when looking at the monitor screen, but they also represent real physical attributes, such as the direction of spin of electrons. When computer memory is erased, then a superficial pattern of information (eg: 010011) is suddenly made uniform (000000) and since this is also a physical system, that physical system is also made uniform and there is a real reduction of entropy which according to the second law of thermodynamics must be associated with a release of high-entropy heat to make sure the entropy of the cosmos increases.

Therefore, Landauer proposed that Maxwell's demon releases heat whenever he clears his memory of the data relating to one molecule in the box in order to look at and study another, and by this deletion he increases the entropy of the cosmos more than he decreases it by sorting molecules by speed. To be specific, Landauer stated that every time a bit (a zero or a one) of information is deleted, an amount E=kTlog2 of (unusable) heat energy is released, where, as above, k is Boltzmann's constant and T is the temperature of the environment. This may all seem like abstract philosophy but this heat release from information has now been measured experimentally, for example by Berut et al.[163] and Jun et al.[164] The cosmos can see information.

161 Landauer, R., 1961. Irreversibility and heat generation in the computing process. *IBM Journal of Research and Development*, 5, 3, 183-191.

162 Gleick, J., 2012. The Information. Fourth Estate.

163 Berut, A., A. Arakalyan, A. Petrosyan, S. Ciliberto, R. Dillenschneider, E. Lutz, 2012. Experimental verification of Landauer's principle linking information and thermodynamics. *Nature*, 483, 187-190

164 Jun, Y., M. Gavrilov, J. Bechhoefer, 2014. High-precision test of Landauer's principle in a feedback trap. *Phys. Rev. Lett.*, 113, 19, 190601.

The importance of this concept of extracting energy from information, I believe, has not yet been appreciated. It is like the realisation by Einstein that it is neither mass that is conserved, nor energy, but mass-energy. This led to the idea that mass and energy are interconvertible, that E=mc^2 and that therefore a lot of energy, E, can be extracted out of a tiny amount of mass, m, because the speed of light squared is such a massive number.

Similarly here, I believe Landauer's principle is telling us that it is not mass or energy that are conserved, but a quantity composed of Energy and Mass and Information. Furthermore, you can derive quantised inertia this way. The equation is: E+mc^2+kTN = constant (where N = bits of information)[165]

8.4 QUANTISED INERTIA FROM INFORMATION

The energy (dE) released by deleting one bit of information is $dE = kT log_2 2$.[166] Deleting N bits gives $E(N) = kT log_2 2^N = kTN$. The figure shows an object, the dashed vertical line. At first it is un-accelerated and sees a cosmic horizon far away: the vertical line on the right. The space it can see has a number of bits (upper horizontal dotted line), each one Planck length long, l_p: the smallest unit of space measurable that we can store one bit in. The object then accelerates leftward, a Rindler horizon forms (middle vertical line) so it sees fewer bits, information has been erased so energy must be released.

$$\Delta E = kT N_1 - kT N_2 = mc^2$$

---

165 McCulloch, M.E. and J. Gine, 2017. Mod. Phys. Lett. A., 32, 28, 1750148.

166 The use of 'log$_2$' instead of 'ln' is compatible with experimental data and information entropy.

N_1 is half the cosmic diameter Θ divided by the Planck length $N_1=\Theta/2l_p$ and N_2 is the distance to the new Rindler horizon divided by the Planck length, $N_2=c^2/al_p$. Putting these into the equation above, using $M=\Delta E/c^2$ and assuming the background is thermalized $E=kT=m_0c^2$ (ie: Unruh radiation)

$$M = m_0 \frac{\Theta}{2l_p}\left(1 - \frac{2c^2}{a\Theta}\right)$$

The extended object has $\Theta/2l_p$ bits so we divide by this to get the mass per Planck length. Bingo! Out comes the formula for quantised inertia![167]

$$m = m_0\left(1 - \frac{2c^2}{a\Theta}\right)$$

This means the energy required for QI behaviour is provided by horizons deleting information. This releases the energy by Landauer's principle.

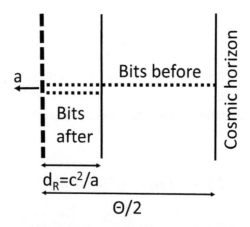

Figure 90. A bit model of QI.

167   See an earlier derivation in McCulloch, M.E., 2020. *Advances in Astrophysics*, 5, 4, 91-94.

CHAPTER 9

INTERLUDE: DARWINIAN PHYSICS

It is argued that physics is the most precise of sciences because of its use of mathematics. This is true, but Darwin's biological idea of natural selection is more attractive in one way than the approach of physics because it needs no arbitrary mathematical laws to be imposed (as if carved on marble blocks in heaven): the laws are determined by the system itself. Maybe physics could be reformulated in this purer form? At the moment the cosmos is assumed to have originated in the free energy miracle of the big bang. This event has been post-dicted (a backwards prediction) by assuming rigid laws stored in some abstract Platonic heaven. Instead, the cosmos may have developed from initial randomness and the predictable phenomena we now see around us are due to the inevitable accumulation of self-repeating phenomena, for example: bound orbits and life, which, once formed, persist and now constitute most of what we see. The initial state is similar to the ancient Egyptian concept of the Ka[168]: the sea of chaos at the beginning of time.

The problem with physics is an enduring legacy from Plato that the laws that govern the world are thought to exist

---

168   Shaw, G.J., 2014. The Egyptian Myths. Thames and Hudson.

independently from nature. For example, we write down New-ton's gravity law or Einstein's field equations and there is some limited empirical backing for them, but they assume a lot, such as the value of the gravitational constant G or the speed of light, c, which have to be input by hand.

Newton used the word 'law' in describing his theories, because that word means a rule that must be followed by humans, so Newton naturally used it to refer to nature's laws which seemed as rigidly applied as the best human ones. For a creative person, Newton was surprisingly strict about laws, as counterfeiters found out when he had them hanged as the Master of the Royal Mint. It is a shame that Newton didn't pick a less rigid word like 'pattern' or 'rule', but that was not his nature. So, we think of the 'laws of physics' which are assumed to exist for eternity and all of nature has to follow them. The predictability of phys-ics has improved and these laws now model, in some sense 4% of the nature we see, but this abstract Platonism remains.

Darwin, in his Origin of Species, proposed a much vaguer idea, but one which goes far deeper than all the laws of physics, and by that I mean that you get much more prediction from a tiny amount of input. Darwin proposed that out of the chaos of random variations in a population, natural selection will select those patterns that best reproduce in that environment and subsequent generations will then be steered by that selection. Applied many times over millions of years this evolution leads to the present complexity of life. Although this idea has not yet developed to be specific enough to make testable predic-tions, there is a lot of good evidence for it and it is far deeper than physics because it is not necessary to have the rules writ-ten down outside of reality in a Platonic way, because the rules are made by interactions within the system itself and are self-evident. In the case of Newton's gravitational law one might ask "So, what makes it that way?" There is no such doubt with natural selection which requires no suspension of disbelief or arbitrary constants, such as G, for acceptance. Once the idea is understood, it is difficult to deny.

To propose an analogy. Imagine an expedition, rather like Darwin's in HMS Beagle that surveys all the islands in the Pacific. They find out that many of these islands don't have animals on them, but those that do have a fixed ratio of predators to prey. There are two ways to approach this: you can either come up with a law that says, if the number of predators is P and the number of prey is Y then P=0.1Y. This is the equivalent of Newton's gravity law. There is of course another way to do it, recognise that the predators and prey exist in symbiosis and if there are too many prey the vegetation is destroyed, and if there are too many predators the prey are destroyed, and then the predators starve. This accounts for all the islands without animals, but the inhabited ones have an acceptable ratio and have stayed in balance all these years. This way of modelling the system is far deeper, involves no assumed parameters and is more predictive. If conditions change, the value of '0.1' might change. The old way would not predict that.

Is it possible to apply this kind of thinking to physics? QI takes a step towards this because G is determined by the cosmic horizon (section 7.3).

This approach also explains why the laws we see are simple, because balances tend to be simple–many effects cancel out in balances.

Something like this was also attempted by Smolin in his 1992 book 'The Life of the Cosmos'[169] where he suggested the idea of 'cosmological natural selection'. The hypothesis is that universes reproduce by creating baby universes inside black holes. The more black holes, the more baby universes, and the more likely it is that the physics from that universe reproduces. Therefore it is more likely that we are inside such a universe,

---

169   Smolin, L., 1999. The Life of the Cosmos. Oxford University Press.

just as it is likely that our biological ancestors were 'fit'. This hypothesis predicts that our universe is likely to be such that it maximises the production of black holes. This was a laudable attempt by Smolin to try and make cosmology predictive, although he said it in the context of string theory (see page 127 in [170]) it could apply to any theory. Another problem is that the physics of black holes is not well understood and not yet testable.

What I'm suggesting here is something far more radical that also requires fewer assumptions and less hidden information. We can imagine a completely random cosmos where things happen according to no laws at all and imagine you are there outside it looking in. All you'd see is chaos, maybe for millions of years, like static on an old TV set.

But, suppose we give each pixel on the TV screen a memory, like the fireflies in Chapter 6, also as in Conway's Game of Life. Then it is certain that eventually a self-repeating process will happen purely by chance. The self-repeating phenomenon is hugely important because as soon as it exists, it will continue forever, unless something external breaks it up. You would now see a pattern inside the chaos. If it can also reproduce, you'd see even more of them. This is similar to Kauffmann's suggestion in which he argues for "Darwin all the way down": that the laws of physics may have evolved by abiotic natural selection[171]. Chaos and randomness is difficult to perceive because it always looks the same, but a repeated process would be suddenly noticeable because it is a pattern. It is no surprise also that we as humans have learned to notice patterns because they are useful: once you know the pattern, you can predict the future, a very useful ability, so it is no surprise that science has learned to focus in

---

170 Smolin, L., 2013. The Trouble with Physics. Allen Lane.

171 Kaufman, Stuart, 2009. Towards a post-reductionist science: the open universe. Arxiv: 0907.2492

on such things as organisms that reproduce, gravity waves and orbits that repeat.

Eventually, for any organism looking on, most of the cosmos would be made up of processes that self-repeat, not only life, but physical processes too, since these are the processes that last to be observed.

As I said above, this is similar to the Conway's game of Life[172] that was very popular back in the 1980s, which applies a set of very simple rules to a grid of cells which can be either black or white, and predicts the occurrence of stable or self-repeating patterns when it is iterated in time.

What I am suggesting then is that the cosmos is inherently random, but each pixel, or firefly, has a memory so that eventually repeatable processes occur and remain, till eventually almost all the cosmos is locked in a repeatable pattern. This means there was not so much a big bang, but more like the chaos often described in early myths, and out of that has grown regularity, and that can be predicted, like Darwinian processes just by using common sense and without arbitrary and rigid laws.

How can this be tested? Maybe in a similar manner to the way evolution is tested, by looking for a past progression of complexity. With the Hubble and James Webb telescopes we can now see many billions of years into the past of the cosmos. This idea predicts that the early universe should show more chaos and simpler balances, the ones producing atoms or hydrogen and helium for example, and then later times should show more complex structures. It should also be possible to predict what structures would be stable in a 3-dimensional cosmos and see whether all of these have been realised.

---

172   Gardner, M., 1970. The fantastic combinations of John Conway's new solitaire game 'life. Mathematical Games. *Scientific American.* Vol. 223, no. 4. pp. 120–123.

People may then argue 'Why, if the universe is not mathematical are these eventually repeated patterns so easily represented using maths?' This model would suggest that it is logically the simplest structures and patterns that are selected first and they are easily expressed using mathematics.

Also, this question is a bit like asking why it is so easy to describe the world we inhabit using words. Of course, the words were developed over many years to describe the world, and so you can't suddenly act with surprise that the world is so describable with words. In the case of maths, it has been developed over millennia to describe the world so it is no wonder that the world 'appears' to be mathematical. It is actually not the case, it is rather that our mathematics is 'worldly'. The difficulty with this question when applied to mathematics is that it is difficult to think of any other way that mathematics could be.

The great advantage of a Darwinian model of physics would be that the rules would be simpler and more fundamental, and all the laws of physics would arise inevitably from them. This would also give us more control over nature. If we believe that P=0.1Y then you can't change a 'constant', but if you realise the underlying causes of the factor 0.1, then you can manipulate it and control nature, and that is what science is for.

Of course, a Theory of Everything (ToE) is impossible. The better our theories get, the more control we will have over the cosmos. Our ToE would then have to predict our own behaviour which takes us beyond science.

CHAPTER 10

APPLICATIONS

10.1 QI THRUST

In this book I have tried to present science as it should be done. First, look at the raw data and seek out and ponder anomalies which undermine the old paradigm. Then you try new theories until you find one that predicts the anomalies and the old data. Finally, you use the new theory to extrapolate useful new technologies. In the case of QI the new technologies are obvious and I'm sure you got a sense of them in the previous section. QI offers a way to get new, clean energy out of the quantum vacuum and a way to produce propellant-less thrust.

At present, in order to make anything move we have to push off something else. This applies to all forms of human transport. A chemical rocket burns fuel and fires hot gas rapidly in one direction so that the cosmic accountant who deals with momentum orders that, to balance his books, the rocket must move the other way. Cars or people, use tyres or feet to push against the Earth. They push the globe one way and move the other. The reason you don't see the whole globe moving when

Figure 91. A horizon (grey squares, metal plate) damping Unruh radiation.

you walk is that it is so massive in comparison to you, but it does move.

Quantised inertia offers a new way to thrust. In Chapter 7, a high acceleration of, especially, electrons was produced in a cavity so that Unruh radiation was produced. Then metal plates were used to damp the Unruh radiation on one side so that the radiation imbalance pushes the cavity or object towards that side. This is illustrated in the schematic. The lighter shades show a higher intensity of Unruh radiation. The darker area has a lower intensity because it is damped by the metal plate (grey squares). So the object (black circle) moves right without the need to expel propellant.

As an oceanographic analogy, imagine a ship in a choppy sea. Waves hit it from all directions. There is no overall thrust. Now imagine you put a 'skirt' on one side of the ship which damps the waves on that side, for example by converting the horizontal momentum that would have hit the side of the ship to vertical stresses in the skirt. The ship will now be pushed more by waves from the other side and will move towards the side with the skirt. This would be a form of marine propulsion that would not require fuel.

The other ocean is that of the vacuum, and its more energetic version: Unruh radiation, and this is available everywhere. Why not use it?

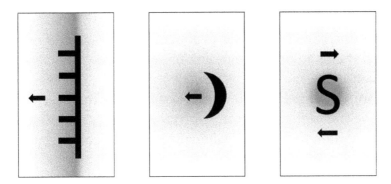

Figure 92. Various structures that could damp Unruh radiation and undergo self-propulsion.

10.2 METAMATERIAL THRUSTERS

As we discussed in many of the above sections, metal plates or baffles can be used to damp Unruh radiation to cause thrust. Slightly more complex arrangements, called metamaterials could also be used.

For example a micro-scale comb-shaped metal would feel a thrust towards its fingers (the left panel) due to the quantum vacuum, if plasmons/electrons were accelerated on its surface so that they see Unruh waves short enough to be damped by the regular spikes.

A boomerang shape should thrust towards its open end (see the central panel) due to the quantum vacuum, a tiny effect, but again if electrons were accelerated then the force would be much larger. I had a student (J. Kerton, 2015) try this as a third year project, using a boomerang shape in a water wave field, and it worked very well.

An S-shape with an axle should rotate towards its pointed ends (see the right panel)[173]. We might call this an S-rotor or a Srotor.

---

173 McCulloch, M.E., 2015. Energy from swastika-shaped rotors. *Progress in Physics*, 11, 2, 139-140.

What metal baffles would be most effective? The need for metal is that the Unruh field produced is composed of random thermal waves so one cannot just fire electromagnetic waves at it to damp it. A metal allows electrons to move in response to the Unruh field and damp it interactively. So, the best damper would be the best conductor. High conductivity materials such as superconductors and graphene would be ideal, perhaps also a plasma.

10.3 GRAPHENE THRUSTER

Graphene is a single layer of carbon atoms and was first discovered by Novoselov, Geim et al., 2004)[174]. It is relatively easy to make with a pencil lead and a bit of sellotape and is among the most conductive materials known. Therefore, it should damp the zero point or Unruh field well.

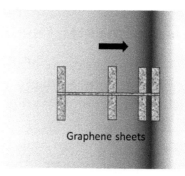

Graphene sheets

Figure 93. The use of graphene to damp Unruh radiation and cause self-propulsion.

A micro-scale thruster could be made by putting together graphene sheets with various degrees of separation so that the closer they are the more they damp the Unruh field as shown in the figure (white to dark). This structure would thrust towards the right, down the gradient in Unruh radiation intensity.

---

174 Novoselov, K.S., A. Geim et al., 2004. Electric Field Effect in Atomically Thin Carbon Films. *Science*, 306, 5696.

10.4 SUPERCONDUCTING THRUSTER

The other highly conductive technology is that of supercon-ductors. If we set up a situation, similar to that tried by Claude Poher (section 5.42) in which we send electrons through a superconductor (the white area in the schematic) and then they hit a normal conductor (grey) they will decelerate (ie: acceler-ate) and produce Unruh waves which will be massively damped (the black area) within the superconductor, in which electrons can move quickly to damp any field.

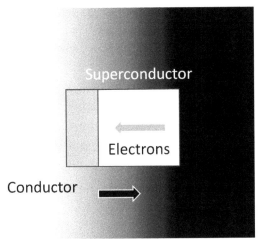

Figure 94. The use of superconductors to damp Unruh radiation and, you guessed it, cause self-propulsion.

The resulting gradient in the Unruh field will push the system in a direction towards the superconductor (see the black arrow).

10.5 PLASMA THRUSTER

A metal damps Unruh radiation, because it allows electrons to move to react to and damp the electromagnetic part of the Unruh field. Superconductors and graphene also do this.

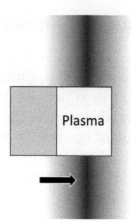

Figure 95. The use of plasma to damp Unruh radiation.

Another method is to use a plasma, which is also composed of free electrons that can move to damp the field.

It could possibly be made from an ion drive, but enclosed so the ions do not escape. For a plasma drive with a power input of say 1kW and a mirrored cavity with a Q of 50 (most mirrors have a reflectivity of 98% or so, leading to a Q of very roughly 50), the thrust would be $F = PQ/c = 0.17mN$, but without fuel.

10.6 FLOATING BRICKS

Another possibility would be to build nanoscale emdrives that will thrust without any input power (see[175]). One way to do this would be to design a material that damps the Unruh radiation spectrum it sees progressively more in one direction, or even just the quantum background itself if the cavities are small enough, see sections 7.37 and 7.38. Imagine applying a high frequency electromagnetic field to accelerate the electrons in

---

175   McCulloch, M.E., 2020. Can nano-materials push off the vacuum? *Progress in Physics*, 16, 12, 73-74.

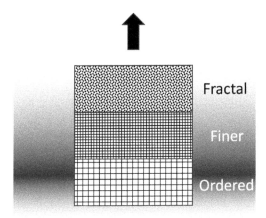

Figure 96. The use of fractal structures to damp Unruh radiation for self-propulsion.

the complex shown on the right here. If the frequency is high enough, then the Unruh waves the electrons see will interact with the structure more at one end than the other so an Unruh gradient will form to push on the structure, as shown in the schematic.

A fractal is a pattern, discovered by Benoit Mandelbrot, that repeats or at least has structure on several scales. A coastline is a fractal such that it gets longer the finer you measure it (see the cartoon). A fractal approach could be used so that the structure at the bottom only damps one (or a few harmonic) Unruh waves whereas the structures higher up have fractal metal shapes that damp a wider range of Unruh wavelengths[176]. This would produce a gradient in the Unruh field that will push the material upwards. This material would then be a 'floating brick', a self-thrusting material. Or, if you place your hand near it, you would feel a force.

---

176   Mentioned in Falling Up, by M.E. McCulloch, 2021. Amazon.

Figure 97. Fractals have many uses.

10.7 ACCELERATION WITHOUT WHIPLASH

With the normal kind of thrust, if you accelerate (a) very fast to the left, see the schematic below right, then the Rindler horizon (black line) you see becomes very close ($d_R = c^2/a$) and the gradient in the Unruh field will push you against an electrostatic force from the floor.

In other words the g-forces can squash you as flat as a pancake. There is a limit to the amount of acceleration humans can stand in spacecraft of around 9g or $88.3 m/s^2$.

However, quantised inertia tells us that if we damp the Unruh radiation in the direction we wish to go, see the dark band in the schematic below, using a metal structure (a damper) to create man-made horizons,

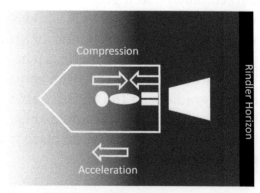

Figure 98. The Unruh field around a rocket.

then the Unruh gradient will pull equally on every object inside the spaceship.[177]

The QI force will then operate to pull the crew of the ship, just as much as the equipment or walls of the craft. Thus we could accelerate even to an extreme degree

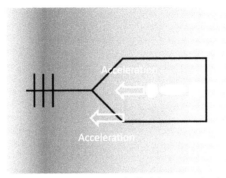

Figure 99. The Unruh field around a horizon drive.

without people or equipment being thrown around or being crushed against the walls by g-forces. Space travel without inertia, therefore with dignity, and no seat belts! The thrusters discussed in section 7.29 and elsewhere in Chapter 10 are of this kind.

10.8 INERTIAL/DEFLECTOR SHIELD–COWCATCHER

This could also solve some of the problems expected from travelling close to the speed of light. At that speed even small dust particles can have a considerable amount of momentum and punch inconvenient holes in your spacecraft. We could use quantised inertia to avoid this if we damped the Unruh field in front of the ship (fewer allowed wavelengths, dark area) using metal baffles or aerials just as in section 10.7 or like the plates of the capacitor in section 7.29 (see the 'III' shapes in the figure) in just the right places so that dust is directed away from the ship. You might call this a deflector shield or to evoke a steam-age metaphor, a cow catcher.

---

177   Again, see Falling Up.

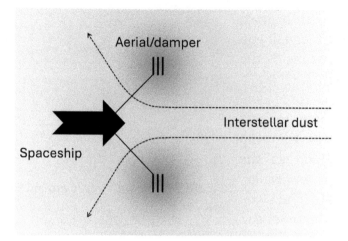

Figure 100. The Unruh field around a spacecraft with a deflector shield.

10.9 ENERGY FROM THE VACUUM

As shown in sections 7.36-7.38, if a cavity is made on the nanoscale (<28 nm) then energy can be extracted from the quantum vacuum. The smaller the cavity the greater the energy released. Normally this energy will do no work, but it could be used to perform work that produces extractable energy, such as the fusion of deuterium to produce heat (7.36) or the direct release of heat or light (7.37, 7.38). Or, it could be as simple as hooking up a QI-thruster to a dynamo. Energy from what we thought was nothing.

This heat release from the vacuum may already be happening in electronic circuits where electrons, or faster-moving plasmons, are forced through wires with very sharp bends. Unruh radiation may be a cause of heating over and above the usual heating due to electrical resistance.

10.10 BEC DRIVE

A Bose-Einstein Condensate (BEC) is formed by cooling a gas (eg Helium-4) of extremely low density, to very near to zero Kelvin. This state was first predicted in 1924 by S.N. Bose and Albert Einstein. One of its properties is that the speed of light in a BEC is very low.

Quantised inertia behaves counterintuitively for very low light speeds. It is usually necessary to have very high accelerations of light to get Unruh waves short enough to 'feel' the cavity and make this work, but interestingly for low light speeds (c) the Rindler horizon at a given acceleration (a) approaches to a distance (d_R) much closer than usual ($d_R = c^2/a$), so in a BEC, even slow light with smaller accelerations would have Unruh waves short enough to interact with the cavity. The BEC would have to fill the whole cavity, but it could boost thrust hugely.[178] Ammonia gas (a dielectric) might be a less effective way to do it.

10.11 CASIMIR PROBE / UNRUH WAVE OBSERVATORY

In section 7.25 we discussed the enhanced Casimir effect, which is one way of explaining QI thrust. The enhancement was caused by high accelerations, so by measuring it we might be able to measure our acceleration. Normally a Casimir cavity feels a force inwards due to the zero point field, but if that field is enhanced because the cavity (or something in it) is itself accelerating and there are extra Unruh waves around it, then the force inwards will be enhanced. The force inwards will have two terms. That due to the normal zero point field and one due to the added Unruh radiation (as in 7.25: $\hbar \rightarrow E\tau \rightarrow kT\tau$).

---

178   The BEC possibility was pointed out to me by Mohan Ahad in 2016.

Then using Unruh's temperature-acceleration relation[179], $kT\tau = \hbar a\tau/2\pi c$) and $\tau = d/c$

$$F = \frac{\hbar c\pi^2 A}{240d^4} + \frac{\hbar a\tau\pi A}{480d^4} = \frac{\hbar\pi A}{240d^4}\left(c\pi + \frac{ad}{2\pi c}\right)$$

Taking the bracket, in order to make the new effect as large as the Casimir effect, setting the two terms equal, we'd need $a=2\pi^2 c^2/d \sim 10^{18}/d$, therefore for a Casimir cavity 1 micron across we'd need $a \sim 10^{24}$ m/s².

Such a Casimir Probe might also make gravity detectable. At present the general relativistic explanation for gravity is bent space. You cannot directly *see* bent space except by passing matter, or light, through it, the modelling of which was the reason bent space was invented in the first place. There is no way to get a second opinion, no direct test. The quantised inertial explanation for gravity (see section 6.5) is a variation of the strength of the Unruh field in space. Unlike the hypothesis of bent space, a Casimir probe could measure this variation of the quantum vacuum and directly test QI-gravity. We just need to place Casimir cavities at different gravitational potentials.

History shows that the more directly testable a theory is, the better.

---

179 $T=\hbar a/2\pi ck$

CHAPTER 11

AN INTERSTELLAR MISSION

11.1 INTRODUCTION

Recent events may have convinced you that it is time to leave the planet. Unfortunately, all the other planets in our Solar system leave something to be desired. Mars is our best bet, and plans for its exploration have been pioneered by Robert Zubrin[180] and recently by Elon Musk, but even Mars is an airless challenge for settlers. Can we go further afield?

According to standard physics and present rocket technology we cannot travel to another Solar system in a human lifetime because we need impractical amounts of heavy fuel to travel fast enough. For example, Voyager 1 is our fastest probe so far. It is travelling at 17 km/s, fast by our standards, but it would still take 75,311 years to get to the nearest star, Proxima Centauri, which is 4.25 light years away. The Parker Solar probe has now exceeded this speed, at 200 km/s, but it did this by diving into the Sun's gravity well, in a similar way to a driver who gets a speeding ticket because he was going down a hill

---

180   Zubrin, R., 1996. The Case for Mars. Touchstone.

(an excellent excuse). To achieve a significant proportion of the speed of light, say 10%, which would get us to Proxima in a human lifetime, at present would require fusion rockets.[181]

There have been some proposals that aim to cut the travel time, for example McNutt et al[182] suggested an interstellar precursor probe called the Innovative Interstellar Explorer. This would use a Radioisotope Thermoelectric Generator (RTG) to power an ion drive, and propel a 1000 kg probe three times faster than Voyager 1, but it would still take 25,000 years to get to Proxima Centauri by which time enthusiasm over the venture might ebb a little, and even the word enthusiasm, or indeed the English language, may not exist. There is something to be said for proposing projects that can be fulfilled in one's own lifetime, in terms of testability, motivation, integrity and self-fulfilment.

The Breakthrough Starshot Program[183] backed by Yuri Milner and Stephen Hawking proposed that nano-craft embedded on 4.1m wide sails could be pushed to Alpha Centauri by a multi-kilometre array of terrestrial lasers with a power of 200 GW. It would take the probes about 20 years to get to Proxima, which sounds more like it, but the laser array would be a gigantic undertaking and the probes would have to be less than a gram in weight (on Earth) and yet would need to include a camera, computer, communications, and a power source! It is also difficult to see how the thin sail would survive impacts from interstellar dust at 0.2c. Engineers like a challenge, but this is extreme and not scale-able for a later human mission.

181 Long, K.F., 2011. Project Icarus: the first unmanned interstellar mission, robotic expansion and technological growth. JBIS, 64, 107-115.

182 McNutt et al., 2002. Innovative Interstellar Explorer. CP 858, Physics of the Heliosheath. Eds. J. Heerikhuisen et al., AIP.

183 Parkin, K.L.G., 2018. The Breakthrough Starshot System Model, *Acta Astronautica*, 152, pp.370-384.

Extrapolating recent trends in the speed of space flight, Long[184] speculated that, at present rates of development, the first unmanned interstellar craft might be launchable by 2100 at the earliest, though he pointed out that an, as yet unknown, technological breakthrough could hasten this significantly.

I propose that QI is that breakthrough. Instead of needing a small planet worth of fuel for chemical rockets, massive fusion ships, multi-kilometre laser arrays or nano-craft it offers propellant-less propulsion. Its fuel is the quantum vacuum itself which is available everywhere and never runs out.

As you have seen in previous sections, QI has been properly verified using astronomical data to a compelling degree. It predicts galaxy rotations, including the smoking-gun cut-off, globular clusters and wide binaries very well, whereas GR, Newton, dark matter and even MoND cannot. Even more crucially, despite some mis-steps that I made over light in cavities, there is evidence that QI thrust has been verified in the laboratory, both emdrives (see section 7.26) and capacitors (7.29, so far, so good).[185] [186]

As has been discussed in section 7.29, the most effective way, so far, to get thrust out of QI is to use highly-accelerated electrons in capacitors. The plates themselves provide the inhomogeneity in Unruh radiation that drives them. Thrust to power ratios of perhaps 10 N/kW have been seen. So what would a QI-based (horizon drive) interstellar probe look like?

First of all, to minimise the cross section exposed to impacts from interstellar dust, the design is elongated, enabling defence from a small and light shield (dotted, right hand side). According

---

184 Long, K.F., 2011. Project Icarus: the first unmanned interstellar mission, robotic expansion and technological growth. *JBIS*, 64, 107-115.

185 Becker and Bhatt, 2018. https://arxiv.org/abs/1810.04368

186 McCulloch and Arundal, 2023. Testing for thrust from quantised inertia. Submitted to EPL.

QI Interstellar Probe

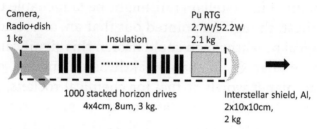

Figure 101. Schematic of an interstellar probe using a horizon drive.

to[187] the thickness of aluminium needed for a craft travelling at 0.3c is 2 cm. So, assuming that the thickness depends on the kinetic energy of impacting particles, and therefore speed squared, for a speed of 0.5c we need a shield with a thickness of 5cm. A shield of aluminium with dimensions of 12.1×12.1cm by 5 cm weighs 2 kg.

The direction of motion is shown by the arrow. One thousand QI capacitor thrusters (of size 4×4 cm and with an 8μm thick dielectric) are shown as paired black lines behind the interstellar dust shield and RTG. They weigh 3 kg in total and should produce 6N of force. Note: they would have to be spaced out far enough that they do not interfere with each others' Rindler horizons. For the laboratory tests this required a 1cm gap.

The power supply needed to maintain the capacitors at equilibrium would depend on the leakage current across them (10^{-6} Amps) times the voltage (1700 V) and then we have to multiply by their number (1000). So, 1.7 W would be needed (more may be available before launch to charge them up quickly). Heating would also be required to keep the capacitors above their

---

187 Hoang, T, A. Lazarian, B. Burkhart, A. Loeb, 2016. The interaction of relativistic spacecraft with the interstellar medium. https://arxiv.org/abs/1608.05284

minimum operating temperature of 50°C. The 1961 SNAP-3B RTG, or a modern variant of it, would provide 52.5 W of thermal power and 2.7W of electrical power, so it should suffice. It weighed 2.1 kg and was 12.1cm in diameter and 14cm high[188]. It is shown by the grey box in the schematic.

We can now work out the acceleration, a, taking into account the relativistic increase of mass with speed (v)

$$a = \frac{F\sqrt{1 - v^2/c^2}}{m}$$

The predicted acceleration, assuming a force of 6 N, and a mass of 8.1 kg (multiplied by 1.03 as a relativistic correction at 0.25c, halfway between 0 and 0.5c) would be 0.72 m/s². At this acceleration the probe would get to 100 AU from the Sun in 75 days, 2000 AU (the start of the Oort cloud) in about one year and achieve a speed of 0.5c in 6.6 years at a distance of 1.6 light years from the Sun. There would be a similar profile for the deceleration near Proxima, leaving us to travel the middle 1 light year at 0.5c, over 2 years. Therefore, the total travel time to Proxima Centauri would be 6.6+2+6.6 = 15.2 years.

In other words, with a horizon drive we can send an unmanned probe to the nearest star in much less than a human lifetime. The thrusts used here are based on those already seen in four labs. Higher thrusts may also be possible by using QI capacitors with smaller separations between the plates (and QI predicts, and allows us to enhance, other thruster methods as well, eg emdrives). The illustrated probe is only one example: better combinations of method, size and power are probable and it may be possible to code an inverse model to predict the best configuration.

---

188 Bennett, G.L., 2006. Space nuclear power: opening the final frontier. 4th International Energy Conversion Eng. Conference and Exhibit (IECEC), June 2006. San Diego, USA.

11.2 COMMUNICATION BACK TO EARTH

The Breakthrough Starshot program proposed[189] utilising the 4.2m diameter light sails of their micro-spacecraft as a laser transmitter. We can do the same though we would need a smaller dish. The signal could be picked up by a large telescope, or by a global array of smaller telescopes.

Another method, also suggested by [190] would be to send more than one craft in a daisy chain. The spacecraft that has arrived at Proxima radios its data to the next in line and the signal is passed down the line back to Earth.

11.3 SUPERLUMINAL COMMUNICATIONS

A more radical communication technique would be to use Unruh waves. We have already discussed the Hartman effect (section 5.39) in which quantum waves can tunnel through obstacles they cannot classically penetrate and that they do this much faster than the speed of light[191]. This provides a possible way to communicate over long distances. According to quantised inertia, complete Unruh waves of longer wavelength than the cosmos cannot exist within it. So, if one made such a wave, which is not impossible since it could be a partial wave, and was able to detect it, again not impossible, then one could communicate across vast distances instantaneously. Given that, $c=f\lambda$, then the frequency required to generate this wave would be about 10^{-19} Hz, way beyond our technology to date.

If this ever became possible it would be a technology similar to the sub-aether in science fiction, and it is a controversial

---

189 Parkin, K.L.G., 2005. A starshot communication downlink. https://arxiv.org/abs/2005.08940

190 Parkin, K.L.G., 2005. " "

191 Hartmann, T.E., 1962. Tunnelling of a wave packet. *Journal of Applied Physics*, 33, 3427.

suggestion because instantaneous communication has to remain consistent with causality.

11.4 A LIGHTER POWER SOURCE

As discussed in sections 7.36–7.38 quantised inertia predicts that the quantum vacuum contained within a metal box of size D will have a temperature of $\hbar c/3kD$, especially if there are electrons that are highly accelerated within the nano-structure. In other words, conductive nano-cavities will have a higher temperature and this heat energy will originate from the vacuum. Heat is already observed to be generated by nano-circuits.

Therefore, if the probe incorporated such a conductive nano-material then heat would be produced from the quantum vacuum and energy could be extracted thermoelectrically, using the large gradient between the 'hot brick' and the cold of space. This would reduce the mass of the craft (no RTG needed), increase the possible acceleration & shorten the trip.

11.5 SELF-THRUSTING INTERSTELLAR DRIVE

It has been proposed in [192] (and section 10.6) that as well as nano-cavities generating heat, they may also produce thrust. The trick here is to make every atom in the material, or most of them, see an Unruh radiation gradient in the same direction. So, a nano-scale series of pyramidal voids might do it, nano-emdrives, with plasmons (surface electrons) travelling over the internal metal surfaces at close to the speed of light. From the reference cited, the size of cavity at which the energy solely from the zero point field ($\hbar$) is enough to produce an acceleration a is

---

192 McCulloch, 2020. Can nano-materials push off the vacuum? *Progress in Physics*, 16, 2, 73-74.

$$L = \sqrt[4]{\frac{2\hbar c}{15\pi\rho\delta a}}$$

Assuming that the density of the metal ρ is 2000kgm^3, its thickness δ is 1mm and the acceleration is 0.64 m/s² (the acceleration of the probe above) then we get L = 178 nm. If we require 9.8 ms^2 for the interstellar probe then we get L = 90 nm. If a material like this could be built on the microscale and incorporated into the probe, then further saving in weight and time could be made.

The earlier tests of QI were against astrophysical data, and QI successfully modelled spacecraft, galaxies and stars in deep space. The cavity applications for thrust and energy follow from the theory, and there is now laboratory evidence too, but in all these terrestrial cases engineering difficulties might arise, that I, as a theorist, may not appreciate, so these proposals should of course be subject to healthy doubt & testing.

CHAPTER 12

CONCLUSION

IN THIS BOOK, I have used the empirical-philosophical approach that has always driven science forward. Physics, as it stands is a great accomplishment, but the anomalies presented here show that in some sense standard physics only predicts 4% of the cosmos. The good news is then that there's plenty of scope for improvement!

Although I cannot guarantee that all the anomalies I mentioned are solid, they are all well documented, and they all point in the same direction: our modern understanding of physics needs revision in the regime where accelerations are extremely low. This is not surprising as those are the deep space regimes that we have only been able to see recently.

In over 25 papers now and three previous books (A textbook: Physics from the Edge[193], and two sci-fi novels: Falling Up[194] and Hacking the Cosmos[195]) and in this book, I have suggested such a revision, called quantised inertia (QI). QI deepens physics

---

193 McCulloch, M.E., 2014. Physics from the Edge. World Scientific.

194 McCulloch, M.E., 2021. Falling Up. Published by KDP, Amazon.

195 McCulloch, M.E., 2023. Hacking the Cosmos or What You Can See is What You Get. KDP, Amazon.

by attributing gravity and inertia to horizon-induced gradients in Unruh radiation (thereby linking relativity and quantum mechanics). It changes Newton's laws slightly by turning inertia & gravity into real quantum forces, the new energy required coming from the deletion of information by horizons.

QI contradicts the constant speed assumption in Newton's First Law since it predicts a (tiny) minimum (quantised) acceleration. It also modifies Newton's second law slightly. However, these changes, though infinitesimal, massively improve empirical predictions in low acceleration regimes. QI is also a more directly testable proposition: Unruh radiation has now been directly seen, in contrast to abstract bent space which can never be. Without arbitrary adjustment, QI predicts many anomalies that other theories cannot, such as galaxy rotation and wide binary orbits. It is conceptually challenging, but it predicts far more than the old physics & is technically simpler, eg: the gravitational constant is no longer needed.

I have argued that quantised inertia gives us a way to extract cheap, clean energy from the vacuum, and produce propellant-less thrust enabling us to get to the nearest star in a travel time on the order of 10 years.

The QI cosmology is not yet complete, so I will just have to write another book about that! Some specific problems to be addressed are:

- Do the details of how Unruh waves interact with horizons have observable consequences?
- Can QI predict particle masses and the strong & weak force?
- Does QI predict all of Arp's quantised redshifts? (Section 7.12)
- Is QI indeed consistent with lensing (Section 7.18) and the bullet cluster?
- How best can we harvest energy and thrust from QI?
- QI eliminates G. Can any other constants be eliminated?

- Derivation of a full QI cosmology–a steady state cosmos?
- Develop informational QI & its philosophy (see Section 8.4)
- Can QI's implication that 'time = change' be tested? (Section 7.5)

One of the aims in writing this book is to persuade others to help answer these questions, and that is where you come in. I invite you to contribute. The formalism I have given QI so far is a theoretical minimum. In the new interplay of information, horizons and the quantum vacuum there is so much to explore and formalise that it could fill lifetimes, and for the applications likewise.

And so, in the end we return to the beginning, but hopefully wiser! The later Graeco-Roman society stopped thinking about real & messy anomalies and reverted to more comfortable discussions disconnected from reality (this is also happening now) and progress in physics slowed down for 1400 years. The new physics presented here is intended to be a reboot of the subject. It is not yet complete but it was inspired by anomalies, is testable, beautiful, simple and will benefit all of us, providing new understanding, clean energies, transport, space exploration & new hope. We cannot possibly imagine what chances will open up and how fascinating it will be.

An anomaly a day keeps stagnation at bay.

ACKNOWLEDGEMENTS

THIS BOOK HAS taken many years to write, well six or so, and it was at one time three separate books, so its history is complex and I've had help and advice from many corners of the world.

Thanks first to Alexander Unzicker who has been a major inspiration to me and who kindly read and commented on this book even while he was on holiday in Ireland. Thanks also to R.C. McCulloch, R. Tattersall, Kelvin Long, B. Kim, H. McCulloch & M. Booth who proofread parts of it, and are always encouraging, and to my energetic editor Robert Zubrin who also read it, suggested many useful corrections, and indeed offered to publish it.

Thanks to DARPA who have provided funding for my efforts and allowed me to devote myself more intensely to quantised inertia for four years.

Thank you to the many other people who have contributed theoretically, financially or experimentally to quantised inertia, such as Keith Pickering, Jaume Gine, Jose Luis Perez-Diaz, Travis Taylor, the Royal Astronomical Society, the Institute of Physics, the International Space Science Institute in Bern, Rick Young, Frank Becker, Ankur Bhatt, Jesus Lucio, Jose Lopez,

Larry Lemke, Richard Arundal and many more, including many on social media.

Last but not least, love and tremendous thanks to my wife for her encouragement, and who also, in taking care of many of the practical aspects of life, has given me some space in which to ponder the big mystery.

–Michael McCulloch
Plymouth, England, April 2024

REFERENCES

1. Allais M.F.C., Mouvement du pendule paraconique et Eclipse totale de Soleil du 30 juin 1954, *C.R. Acad. Sci.* 245 (1957) 2001.

2. Allais M.F.C., L'anisotropie de l'espace (Clement Juglar, Paris, 1997).

3. Allais, M.F.C., 1999. The Allais Effect: and my experiments with the paraconical pendulum 1954-1960. A memoir prepared for NASA.

4. Anasova, J., V.V. Orlov and N.A. Pavlova.: *Astronomy and Astrophysics* (1994), 292, 115 (1994).

5. Anderson, J.D., P.A. Laing, E.L. Lau, A.S. Liu, M.M. Nieto and S.G. Turyshev, 1998. Indication from Pioneer, 10/11, Galileo & Ulysses data of an apparent weak anomalous, long range acceleration. *Phys. Rev. Lett.*, 81, 2858-2861. https://arxiv.org/abs/gr-qc/9808081

6. Anderson, J.D., J.K. Campbell, J.E. Ekelund, J. Ellis, J.F. Jordan, 2008. Anomalous Orbital-Energy Changes Observed during Spacecraft Flybys of Earth. *Phys. Rev. Lett.*, 100, 091102. https://doi.org/10.1103/PhysRevLett.100.091102

7.   Anderson, J.D, G. Schubert, V. Trimble and M.R. Feldman, 2015. Measurements of Newton's gravitational constant and the length of day. *EPL*, 110, 10002. https://arxiv.org/abs/1504.06604

8.   Arita, Y., M. Mazilu and K. Dholakia, 2013. Laser-induced rotation and cooling of a trapped microgyroscope in vacuum. *Nature Communications*. DOI:10.1038/ncomms3374. https://www.nature.com/articles/ncomms3374

9.   Arp, Halton, 1998. Seeing Red: redshifts, cosmology and academic science. Apeiron Press.

10. Aspect, A., 1999. Bell's inequality test: more real than ever. *Nature*, Vol. 398. 189-190. https://www.nature.com/articles/18296

11. Batygin, K. and M.E. Brown, 2016. Evidence for a distant giant planet in the Solar system. *Astronomical Journal*, 151, 22. https://iopscience.iop.org/article/10.3847/0004-6256/151/2/22

12. Becker, F.M. and A.S. Bhatt, 2018. Electrostatic accelerated electrons within symmetric capacitors during eld emission condition events exert bidirectional propellant-less thrust. https://arxiv.org/abs/1810.04368

13. Bennett, G.L., 2006. Space nuclear power: opening the final frontier. 4th International Energy Conversion Eng. Conference and Exhibit (IECEC), June 2006. San Diego, USA.

14. Berut, A., A. Arakalyan, A. Petrosyan, S. Ciliberto, R. Dillenschneider, E. Lutz, 2012. Experimental verification of Landauer's principle linking information and thermodynamics. *Nature*, 483, 187-190. https://www.nature.com/articles/nature10872

15. Bethe, H.A. and W. Heitler, 1934. On the stopping of fast particles and on the creation of positive electrons. Proc. Phys. Soc. Lond. 146, 83 112.

16. Bianchi, C., and A. Meloni, 2009. Natural and man-made terrestrial electromagnetic noise: an outlook. Annals of Geophysics, 50(3).

17. Biretta, J.A., W.B. Sparks, F. Macchetto, 1999. Hubble space telescope observations of superluminal motion in the M87 jet. *Astrophysical Journal*, 520, 621-626. https://iopscience.iop.org/article/10.1086/307499

18. Blackett, P.M.S. and G.P.S. Occhialini, 1933. Some photographs of the tracks of penetrating radiation. Proc. R. Soc. London, A 139, 839, 699-726.

19. Brady, D.A., H.G. White, P. March, J.T. Lawrence and F.J. Davies, 2014. Anomalous thrust production from an RF test device measured on a low-thrust torsion pendulum. 50th AIAA/ASME/SAE/ASEE Joint Propulsion conference.

20. Braga, M.H. M.S. Chandrasekar, A.J., Murchison, J,B. Goodenough, 2018. Non-traditional, Safe, High Voltage Rechargeable Cells of Long Cycle Life. *Journal of the American Chemical Society*. 140 (20), 6343–6352.

21. Brennen, M.P., S. Hilgenfeldt and D. Lohse, 2002. Single-bubble sonoluminescence. *Rev. Modern Phys.*, Vol 74, 2, 425-484. https://doi.org/10.1103/RevModPhys.74.425

22. Briggs, A., 2020. What is a Magnetar? Earth Sky Magazine.

23. Brooks, M., 2005. 13 Things That Do Not Make Sense. New Scientist.

24. Campbell, G.K., A. E. Leonhardt, J. Mun, M. Boyd, E. W. Streed, W. Ketterle; D. E. Pritchard, 2005. Photon recoil

momentum in dispersive media. Physical Review Letters. 94 (17). https://journals.aps.org/prl/abstract/10.1103/PhysRevLett.94.170403

25. Canning, F.X., C. Melcher, W. Winet, 2004. Asymmetrical capacitors for propulsion. NASA/CR-2004-213312. https://ntrs.nasa.gov/citations/20040171929

26. Cardone, F., R. Mignani, M. Monti, A. Petrucci and V. Sala, 2012. Piezonuclear Neutrons from Iron. *Modern Physics Letters A.*, 27, 18, 1250102. https://www.worldscientific.com/doi/10.1142/S0217732312501027

27. Cook, N., 2001. The Hunt for Zero Point. Arrow Books.

28. Crockett, C., 2019. What's hotter than the surface of the Sun? The Solar corona. *Astronomy*. Sept 25th.

29. Davies, P.C.W., 1975. Scalar production in Schwarzschild and Rindler metrics. J. Phys. A., 8, 609-616. https://iopscience.iop.org/article/10.1088/0305-4470/8/4/022

30. Dicke, R.H, 1970. Gravitation & the Universe: Jayne Lectures for 1969. American Philosophical Society.

31. Dirac, P.A.M., 1937. The Cosmological Constants. *Nature*. 139 (3512): 323. https://www.nature.com/articles/139323a0

32. Duif, C.P., 2004. A review of conventional explanations of anomalous observations during Solar eclipses. https://arxiv.org/abs/gr-qc/0408023

33. Einstein, A. and O. Stern, 1913. *Annalen der Physik*, 40, 551-60. https://myweb.rz.uni-augsburg.de/~eckern/adp/history/einstein-papers/1913_40_551-560.pdf

34. Einstein, A., Podolsky, B., Rosen, N., 1935. Can Quantum-Mechanical Description of Physical Reality Be Considered Complete? *Physical Review*. 47 (10): 777–780.

35. Farman, J.C., B.G. Gardiner and J.D. Shanklin, 1985. Large losses of total ozone in Antarctica reveal seasonal ClOx/NOx interaction. *Nature*, 315, 6016, 207-210. https://www.nature.com/articles/315207a0

36. Farrington, B., 1944. Greek Science. Pelican.

37. Fleischmann, M., Pons, S., 1989. Electrochemically induced nuclear fusion of deuterium. *Journal of Electroanalytical Chemistry*, 261 (2A): 301–308.

38. Freedman, W.L., 2001. Final results of the Hubble space Telescope key project to measure the Hubble constant. *Astrophys. J.*, 553, 47-72.

39. Fleischmann, M., S. Pons and M. Hawkins, 1989. Electrochemically induced nuclear fusion of deuterium. *J. Electroanal. Chem.*, 261, 301-308 and errata in 263, 187-188. https://doi.org/10.1016/0022-0728(89)80006-3

40. Fulling, S.A., 1973. Nonuniqueness of canonical field quantization in Riemannian space-time. Phys. Rev. D., 7, 2850-2862. https://journals.aps.org/prd/abstract/10.1103/PhysRevD.7.2850

41. Gardner, Martin, 1970. The fantastic combinations of John Conway's new solitaire game 'life'. Mathematical Games. *Scientific American*. Vol. 223, no. 4. pp. 120–123.

42. Genzel, R., et al., 2017. Strongly baryon-dominated disk galaxies at the peak of galaxy formation ten billions years ago. *Nature*, 543, 397-401. https://arxiv.org/abs/1703.04310

43. Gine, J., and M.E. McCulloch, 2016. Inertia from Unruh temperatures. Modern Physics Letters A., 31, 1650107. https://www.worldscientific.com/doi/abs/10.1142/S0217732316501078

44. Gleick, J., 2012. The Information. Fourth estate.

45. Hartmann, T.E., 1962. Tunnelling of a wave packet. *Journal of Applied Physics*, 33, 3427.

46. Hawking, S.W., 1976. Particle creation by black holes. *Comm. Math. Phys.* 43, 199-220. https://link.springer.com/article/10.1007/BF02345020

47. Hawkins, M.R.S., 2010. On time dilation in quasar light curves. *Mon. Not. Royal Astro. Soc.*, 405, 1940-1946. https://academic.oup.com/mnras/article/405/3/1940/967150

48. Hayasaka, H., H. Tanaka, T. Hashida, T. Chubachi and T. Sugiyama, 1997. Possibility for the existence of anti-gravity: evidence from a free-fall experiment using a spinning gyro. *Speculations in Science and Technology*, 20, 173-181.

49. Hernandez, X., R.A.M. Cortes, C. Allen and R. Scarpa, 2018. Challenging a Newtonian Prediction through GAIA wide binaries. *International Journal of Modern Physics D*, Volume 28, Issue 8, id. 1950101. https://arxiv.org/abs/1810.08696

50. Hernandez, X., S. Cookson, RAM, Cortes, 2022. Internal kinematics of Gaia eDR3 wide binaries. *MNRAS*, 509, 2, 2304-2317. https://academic.oup.com/mnras/article/509/2/2304/6412540

51. Hoag A.A., 1950. A peculiar object in Serpens. *Astronomical Journal.* 55: 170.

52. Hoang, T, A. Lazarian, B. Burkhart, A. Loeb, 2016. The interaction of relativistic spacecraft with the interstellar medium. https://arxiv.org/abs/1608.05284.

53. Jennison, R.C., 1979. What is an electron? A new model: the phase locked cavity. *Wireless World.* June 1979.

54. Jun, Y., M. Gavrilov, J. Bechhoefer, 2014. High-precision test of Landauer's principle in a feedback trap. *Phys.*

Rev. Lett., 113, 19, 190601. https://journals.aps.org/prl/abstract/10.1103/PhysRevLett.113.190601

55. Kallivayalil, N. et al., 2013. Third-epoch Magellanic Cloud Proper Motions. I. Hubble Space Telescope/WFC3 Data and Orbit Implications. Third-epoch Magellanic Cloud Proper Motions. I. Hubble Space Telescope/WFC3 Data and Orbit Implications

56. Kaufman, S., 2009. Towards a post-reductionist science: the open universe. https://arxiv.org/abs/0907.2492

57. Kim, S., H-S Lee, B. Jang and S. Cho, 2016. Strain-controlled nanocrack formation in a Pd lm on polydimethylsiloxane for the detection of low H2 concentrations. *J. Mater. Sci.*, 51, 9, 4530-4537.

58. Klein, N., 2016. Are gravitational constant measurement discrepancies linked to galaxy rotation curves? https://arxiv.org/abs/1610.09181

59. Kragh, H., 2011. Preludes to dark energy: zero-point energy and vacuum speculations. https://arxiv.org/abs/1111.4623

60. Krasznahorkay et al. (2016). Observation of Anomalous Internal Pair Creation in 8Be: A Possible Indication of a Light, Neutral Boson. *Physical Review Letters*, 116, 042501.

61. Landauer, R., 1961. Irreversibility and heat generation in the computing process. *IBM Journal of Research and Development*, 5, 3, 183-191.

62. LHCb Collaboration, 2022. Test of lepton universality in beauty-quark decays. *Nature Physics* 18, (2022) 277-282.

63. Lin S-Y., 2020. An in situ and direct confirmation of super-Planckian thermal radiation emitted from

a metallic photonic-crystal at optical wavelengths. *Scientific Reports*, 10, 5209.

64. Loeb, A., 2021. Extraterrestrial: the first sign of intelligent life beyond Earth. HMHBooks.

65. Long, K.F., 2011. Project Icarus: the first unmanned interstellar mission, robotic expansion and technological growth. *JBIS*, 64, 107-115.

66. Lynch, M.H., E. Cohen, Y. Hadad & I. Kaminer, 2021. Experimental Observation of Acceleration-Induced Thermality. *Phys. Rev. D*. 104, 025015. https://arxiv.org/abs/1903.00043

67. Mahood T.L., 1999. Propellent-less propulsion: recent experimental results exploiting transient mass modification. STAIF-2000. AIP, 1014-20.

68. March, P. and A. Palfreyman, 2006. The Woodward Effect: Math Modeling and Continued Experimental Verifications at 2 to 4 MHz. STAIF-2006, AIP Conference Proceedings, Volume 813, pp. 1321-1332

69. Martins A.A., and M.J. Pinheiro, 2011. On the propulsive force developed by an asymmetric capacitors in a vacuum. SPESIF-2011. *Physics Procedia*, 20, 112-119. https://www.sciencedirect.com/science/article/pii/S1875389211005797

70. Matthews, R., G. Gilmore, 1993. Is Proxima really in orbit about α Cen A/B? *Mon. Not. Royal Astro. Soc.*, Vol. 261, 1, L5-L7. https://academic.oup.com/mnras/article/261/1/L5/1001127

71. Meurer et al., 2018. Cosmic clocks: A Tight Radius–Velocity Relationship for HI-Selected Galaxies. *MNRAS*, 476, 1624-1636. https://arxiv.org/abs/1803.04716

72. McCulloch, M.E., J.O.S. Alves & M.J. Bell, 2004. Modelling shallow mixed layers in the northeast Atlantic.

J. Marine Systems, Vol. 52(1-4), pp 107-119. https://www.sciencedirect.com/science/article/abs/pii/S0924796304001034

73.   McCulloch, M.E., 2007. The Pioneer anomaly as modified inertia. *MNRAS*, 376, 338-342. https://academic.oup.com/mnras/article/376/1/338/973651

74.   McCulloch, M.E., 2008. Can the flyby anomalies be explained by a modification of inertia? *JBIS*, Vol. 61, 373-378.

75.   McCulloch, M.E., 2008. Modelling the flyby anomalies using a modification of inertia. *MNRAS Letters*, 389 (1), L57-60. https://academic.oup.com/mnrasl/article/389/1/L57/996711

76.   McCulloch, M.E., 2010. Minimum accelerations from quantised inertia. *EPL*, 90, 29001. https://iopscience.iop.org/article/10.1209/0295-5075/90/29001 / https://arxiv.org/abs/1004.3303

77.   McCulloch, M.E., 2011. The Tajmar effect from quantised inertia. *EPL*, 95, 39002. https://iopscience.iop.org/article/10.1209/0295-5075/95/39002 / https://arxiv.org/abs/1106.3266

78.   McCulloch, M.E., 2011. Can the Podkletnov effect be explained by quantised inertia? Physics Procedia, 20, 134-139. https://www.sciencedirect.com/science/article/pii/S1875389211005815 / https://arxiv.org/abs/1108.3488

79.   McCulloch, M.E., 2012. Testing quantised inertia on galactic scales. *Astrophys. Space Sci*, 342, 2, 575-578. https://link.springer.com/article/10.1007/s10509-012-1197-0 https://arxiv.org/abs/1207.7007

80.   McCulloch, M.E., 2013. Inertia from an asymmetric Casimir effect. *EPL*, 101, 59001. https://iopscience.iop.

org/article/10.1209/0295-5075/101/59001 https://arxiv.org/abs/1302.2775

81. McCulloch, M.E., 2014. Gravity from the uncertainty principle. *Astrophys. & Space Sci.*, 349, 957-959. https://link.springer.com/article/10.1007/s10509-013-1686-9 https://www.researchgate.net/publication/260941358_Gravity_from_the_uncertainty_principle

82. McCulloch, M.E., 2014. A toy cosmology using a Hubble-scale Casimir effect. *Galaxies*, 2, 1, 81-88. https://www.mdpi.com/2075-4434/2/1/81

83. McCulloch, M.E., 2014. Physics from the Edge. World Scientific.

84. McCulloch, M.E., 2015. Testing quantised inertia on the emdrive. *EPL*, 111, 60005. https://arxiv.org/abs/1604.03449

85. McCulloch, M.E., 2015. Energy from swastika-shaped rotors. *Progress in Physics*, 11, 2, 139-140. https://ptep-online.com/2015/PP-41-08.PDF

86. McCulloch, M.E., 2016. Quantised inertia from relativity and the uncertainty principle. *EPL*, 115, 69001. https://iopscience.iop.org/article/10.1209/0295-5075/115/69001 https://arxiv.org/abs/1610.06787

87. McCulloch, M.E., 2017. Low acceleration dwarf galaxies as tests of quantised inertia. *Astrophys. & Space Sci.*, 362, 57. https://link.springer.com/article/10.1007/s10509-017-3039-6 https://arxiv.org/abs/1703.01179

88. McCulloch, M.E., 2017. Galaxy rotation from quantised inertia and visible mass only. *Astrophys. & Space Sci.*, 362, 149. https://link.springer.com/article/10.1007/s10509-017-3128-6 https://arxiv.org/abs/1709.04918

89. McCulloch, M.E., 2017. Testing quantised inertia on emdrives with dielectrics. *EPL*, 118, 34003. https://iopscience.iop.org/article/10.1209/0295-5075/118/34003

90. McCulloch, M.E., and J. Gine, 2017. Modified inertial mass from information loss. *Mod. Phys. Lett. A.*, 32, 1750148. https://www.researchgate.net/publication/319487604_Modified_inertial_mass_from_information_loss

91. McCulloch, M.E., 2018. Can cold fusion be explained by quantised inertia? *Progress in Physics*, Vol. 14, 2, 63-65. https://ptep-online.com/2018/PP-53-02.PDF

92. McCulloch, M.E., 2018. Propellant-less propulsion from quantised inertia. *J Space Explor*, 7(3), 151-. https://www.tsijournals.com/articles/propellantless-propulsion-from-quantized-inertia.pdf

93. McCulloch, M.E., 2019. Can we hide gravitational sources behind Rindler horizons? *Progress in Physics*, 15, 2. https://ptep-online.com/2019/PP-57-05.PDF

94. McCulloch, M.E., 2019. Superluminal travel from quantised inertia. *J. Space Exploration*. 8, 2. https://www.tsijournals.com/articles/superluminal-travel-from-quantised-inertia.pdf

95. McCulloch, M.E. & J. Lucio, 2019. Testing Newton/GR, MoND & quantised inertia on wide binaries. *Astrophys. & Space Sci*, 364, 121. https://link.springer.com/article/10.1007/s10509-019-3615-z

96. McCulloch M.E., & J. Gine, 2020. Deriving quantised inertia using horizon-widths in the uncertainty principle. *Adv. St. Theor. Phys.*, 14, 1, 1-8.

97. McCulloch, M.E., 2020. Can nano-materials push off the vacuum? *Progress in Physics*, 16, 73-74. https://ptep-online.com/2020/PP-60-02.PDF

98. McCulloch, M.E., 2020. Quantised inertia and galaxy rotation from information theory. *Advances in Astrophysics*, 5, 4, 91-94. http://www.isaacpub.org/4/2050/5/4/11/2020/AdAp.html

99. McCulloch, M.E. & J. Gine, 2021. The EPR paradox & the uncertainty principle. *Modern Phys. Letters–B*, 35, 4, 2150072. https://www.worldscientific.com/doi/10.1142/S021798492150072X

100. McCulloch, M.E., 2021. Falling Up: How to Get to Proxima Centauri. Published by KDP, Amazon. https://www.amazon.com/Falling-Up-How-Proxima-Centauri/dp/1739893603

101. McCulloch, M.E., 2022. Testing QI on the bending of light by the Sun. Research Square. https://www.researchsquare.com/article/rs-2251614/v1

102. McCulloch, M.E. & R. Arundal, B.Kim & J. Graham-Jones, 2023. Testing for thrust from quantised inertia. Submitted to *EPL*.

103. McCulloch, M.E., 2023. Hacking the Cosmos: What You Can See is What You Get. KDP, Amazon. https://www.amazon.com/Hacking-Cosmos-What-You-Can/dp/1739893611

104. McNutt, R.L., R.E. Gold, T. Krimigis, E.C. Roelof, M. Gruntman, G. Gloekcer, P.L. Koehn, W.S. Kurth, S.R. Oleson, D.I. Fiehler, M. Haranyi, R.A Mewalt ,J.C. Leary and B.J. Anderson, 2003. Innovative Interstellar Explorer. CP 858, Physics of the Heliosheath. Editors: J. Heerikhuisen et al., AIP.

105. Meurer et al., 2018. Cosmic clocks: A Tight Radius–Velocity Relationship for HI-Selected Galaxies *MNRAS*, 476, 1624-1636. https://academic.oup.com/mnras/article/476/2/1624/4925565

106. Meyer, H.O, 2010. Spontaneous electron emission from a cold surface. *EPL*, 89, 58001.

107. Micheli, et al., 2018. Non-gravitational acceleration in the trajectory of 1I/2017 U1 'Oumuamua'. *Nature*, 559, 223-226. https://www.researchgate.net/publication/326018112_Non-gravitational_acceleration_in_the_trajectory_of_1I2017_U1_'Oumuamua

108. Milgrom, M., 2005. In Mass profiles and shapes of cosmological structures. G. Mamon, F. Combes, C. Deffayet, B. Fort (Editors.). EAS Publications Series Vol. 20, EDP Sciences, Lex Ulix Cedex A, p 217.

109. Moddel, G., A. Weerakkody, D. Doroski, D. Bartusiak, 2021. Optical cavity induced current. *Symmetry*, 13, 517.

110. Neunzig, O., M. Weikert and M. Tajmar, 2021. Thrust measurements and evaluation of asymmetric infrared laser resonators for space propulsion. CEAS Space Journal. DOI: 10.1007/s12567-021-00366-4 https://link.springer.com/article/10.1007/s12567-021-00366-4

111. Novoselov, K.S., A. Geim et al., 2004. Electric Field Effect in Atomically Thin Carbon Films. *Science*, 306, 5696.

112. Nunez, C., 2019. Ball lightning: weird, mysterious perplexing & deadly. *National Geographic*. March 5th.

113. Olenici, D., 2017. Anomalies in pendulum behaviour observed during conjunctions of Mercury/Sun on 11th November 2006, 14th July 2009 and 17 November 2015. Advances in Astrophysics, 1, 1, 22.

114. Pais, A., 1982. Subtle is the Lord. Oxford Books.

115. Paiva, G.S., C.A. Taft, 2010. A hypothetical dusty plasma mechanism for the Hesdallen lights. *J. Atmos. And Solar-Terrestrial Physics*. 72, 16, 1200-1203.

116. Parkin, K.L.G., 2005. A starshot communcation downlink. https://arxiv.org/abs/2005.08940

117. Parkin, K.L.G., 2018. The Breakthrough Starshot System Model, *Acta Astronautica*, 152, pp.370-384.

118. Penzias, A.A., R.W. Wilson, 1965. A Measurement of Excess Antenna Temperature At 4080 Mc/s. *Astrophysical Journal Letters*. 142: 419–421.

119. Planck Collaboration, 2014. Planck 2013 results: CMB power spectrum and likelihood. *Astronomy and Astrophysics*, 571, A15.

120. Podkletnov, E.E. and R. Nieminen, 1992. A possibility of gravitational shielding by bulk YBa2Cu3O7-x superconductor. *Physica C*, 203, 441-444.

121. Podkletnov, E.E., 1997. Weak gravitational shielding properties of composite bulk YBa2Cu307-x superconductor below 70K under e.m. eld. Arxiv: condmat/9701074v3.

122. Podkletnov, E., G. Modanese, 2001. https://arxiv.org/abs/physics/0108005

123. Poher, C., D. Poher and P. Marquet, 2010. Propelling phenomenon revealed by electric discharges into layered Y123 superconducting ceramics. *Eur. Phys. J. Appl. Phys.*, 50, 30803 (suspended).

124. Pohl, R. et al., 2010. The size of the proton. *Nature*, 466, 213.

125. Porcas, R., 1983. Superluminal motions: Astronomers still puzzled. *Nature*, 302 (5911): 753. doi:10.1038/302753a0.

126. Poston, D.I., R.J. Kapernick and R.M. Guffee, 2002. Design and analysis of the SAFE-400 space fission reactor. *AIP Conference Proc.*, Vol., 608, p. 578.

127. Pugach, A.F and D. Olenici, 2012. Observations of correlated behaviour of two light torsion balances and a paraconical pendulum in separate locations during the Solar eclipse of January 26th, 2009. *Advances in Astronomy* ,Vol. 2012, 263818.

128. Quinn, T., C. Speake & R. Davis, 2013. Improved Determination of G Using Two Methods. *Phys. Rev. Lett.*, 101102.

129. Ramos, R., D. Spierlings, I. Racicot, A.M. Steinberg, 2020. Measurement of the time spent by a tunnelling atom within the barrier region. *Nature*, 583, 529-532. https://www.researchgate.net/publication/343142291_Measurement_of_the_time_spent_by_a_tunnelling_atom_within_the_barrier_region

130. Rancourt, L.J., 2011. Effect of light on gravitational attraction. *Physics Essays*. 24(4), 557-

131. Rancourt, L., 2015. Further experiments demonstrating the effect of light on gravitation. *Applied Physics Res.*, 7, 4, 4-13.

132. Rees, M., 1966. Appearance of relativistically expanding radio sources. *Nature*, 211, 5048. https://www.nature.com/articles/211468a0

133. Riess, A.G.; et al., 1998. Observational Evidence from Supernovae for an Accelerating Universe and a Cosmological Constant. *The Astronomical Journal*. 116 (3): 1009–1038.

134. Riess, A. et al., 2019. Large Magellanic Cloud Cepheid Standards Provide a 1% Foundation for the Determination of the Hubble Constant and Stronger

Evidence for Physics beyond ΛCDM. *The Astrophysical Journal*, Volume 876, Issue 1, article id. 85, 13 pp.

135. Robataille, P-M., 2007. WMAP: A radiological analysis. Progress in Physics, Vol. 1.

136. Robataille, P-M., 2007. On the origins of the CMB. *Progress in Physics*, Vol. 1.

137. Rubin, V.C.; Ford, W. Kent, Jr., 1970. Rotation of the Andromeda Nebula from a Spectroscopic Survey of Emission Regions. *The Astrophysical Journal*. 159: 379–403.

138. Scarpa, R., G. Marconi, R. Gilmozzi and G. Carrano, 2007. Using globular clusters to test gravity in the weak acceleration regime. *The Messenger*, 128 ,41-. https://arxiv.org/abs/0707.2459

139. Serebrov, A. et al., 2005. Measurement of the neutron lifetime using a gravitational trap and a low-temperature Fomblin coating. *Physics Letters B*, Volume 605, Issue 1-2, p. 72-78.

140. Segransan, D., et al., 2003. First radius measurements of very low mass stars with the VLTI. *Astronomy and Astrophysics*, 397, 3, L5-L8 (2003).

141. Shaw, G.J., 2014. The Egyptian Myths: a guide to the ancient gods and legends. Thames and Hudson.

142. Shawyer, R, 2008. Microwave propulsion—progress in the emdrive programme. 59th International Astronautical Conference. IAC-2008. Glasgow, UK.

143. Shawy-Yu Lin, 2020. An in-situ and direct Confirmation of Super-Planckian Thermal Radiation Emitted from a Metallic Photonic-Crystal at Optical Wavelengths. *Scientific Reports*, 10, Art. Number 5209.

144. She, J., Yu. Feng, 2008. Observation of a push force on the end face of a nanometer silica filament exerted by outgoing light. *Phys. Rev. Lett.* 101 (24): 243601.

145. Schlamminger, S., 2014. Reflections on a measurement of the gravitational constant using a beam balance and 13 tons of mercury. *Phil. Trans. Roy. Soc.*, 372, 20140027. https://royalsocietypublishing.org/doi/pdf/10.1098/rsta.2014.0027

146. Smolin, L., 1999. The Life of the Cosmos. Oxford University Press.

147. Smolin, L., 2013. Time reborn. Allen Lane.

148. Stoltzenberg, M., and T.C, Marshall, 2008. Charge structure and dynamics in thunderstorms. *Space Science Reviews*, 137, 1-4, 355-372.

149. Tajmar, M., O. Neunzig and M. Weikert, 2021. *CEAS Space Journal*, 14, 31-44.

150. Taylor, T.T., 2017. Propulsive forces using High-Q asymmetric high energy laser resonators. *JBIS*, 70, 238-243.

151. Tempel E., R. S. Stoica, E. Saar, 2013. Evidence for spin alignment of spiral and elliptical/S0 galaxies in filaments. *Monthly Notices of the Royal Astronomical Society*, Vol. 428, Issue 2, 11, Pages 1827–1836.

152. Trujillo C.A and S.S. Shepard, 2014. A Sedna-like body with a perihelion of 80 AU. *Nature*, 507, 471.

153. Tully, R.B. and J.R. Fisher, 1977. A new method of determining distance to galaxies. *Astronomy and Astrophysics*, 661-673.

154. Turyshev, S. et al., 2012. Support for the Thermal Origin of the Pioneer Anomaly. Phys. Rev. Lett. 108, 241101

155. Uebler, H., et al., 2017. The evolution of the Tully-Fisher relation between z=2.3 and z=0.9 with KMOS. *Astrophysical Journal*, 842, 2, 121.

156. Unruh, W.G., 1976. Notes on black hole evaporation. *Phys. Rev. D.*, 14, 870. https://journals.aps.org/prd/abstract/10.1103/PhysRevD.14.870

157. Unzicker, A., 2007. Why do we still believe in Newton's laws? Facts, myths and methods in gravitational physics. https://arxiv.org/abs/gr-qc/0702009

158. Unzicker, A., 2013. The Higgs Fake.

159. Unzicker, A., 2015. Einstein's Lost Key.

160. Unzicker, A., 2019. The Mathematical Reality.

161. Vincent, J., et al., 2007. Experimental Realization of Wheeler's Delayed-Choice Gedanken Experiment. *Science*, Vol. 315, Issue 5814, pp. 966-968.

162. Wilson, C.M., G. Johansson, A. Pourkabirian, M. Simoen, J.R. Johansson, T. Duty, F. Nori and P. Delsing, 2011. Observation of the dynamical Casimir effect in a superconducting circuit. *Nature*, 479, p376 https://arxiv.org/abs/1105.4714

163. White, H., P. March, J. Lawrence, J. Vera, A. Sylvester, D. Brady and P. Bailey, 2017. Measurement of Impulsive Thrust from a Closed Radio-Frequency Cavity in Vacuum. *J. Propulsion and Power*, 33, 830. https://arc.aiaa.org/doi/10.2514/1.B36120

164. Woodward, J., 1990. A new experimental approach to Mach's principle and relativistic gravitation. *Foundations of Physics Letters*, 3, 497-506.

165. Ziebart, M, A. Sibthorpe, P. Cross, Y. Bar-Sever, B. Haines, 2007. Cracking the GPS-SLR orbit anomaly. Proceedings of ION-GNSS-2007, Fort Worth, Session, F-4, p2033-2038.

166. Zubrin, R., 1996. The Case for Mars. Touchstone.
167. Zwicky, F., 1933. Die Rotverschiebung von extragalaktischen Nebeln [The red shift of extragalactic nebulae]. *Helvetica Physica Acta*. 6: 110–127.

THE END